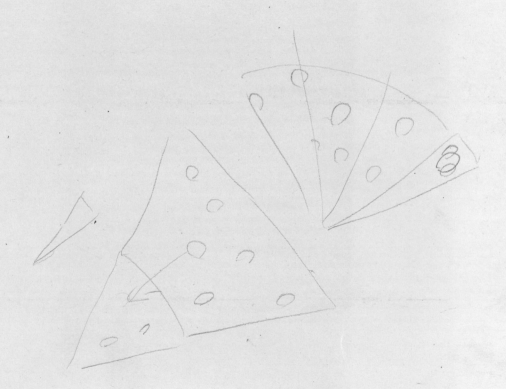

HANDBOOK OF BOTANICAL DIAGRAMS

HANDBOOK OF
BOTANICAL DIAGRAMS

By

BLODWEN LLOYD, Ph.D., M.Sc.

Senior Lecturer in the Department of Microbiology
and Botany, Royal Technical College, Glasgow

UNIVERSITY OF LONDON PRESS LTD.
WARWICK SQUARE, LONDON, E.C.4

FIRST PRINTED 1935
SECOND EDITION 1949
REPRINTED 1956, 1958

Printed & Bound in England for the UNIVERSITY OF LONDON PRESS, LTD.,
by HAZELL WATSON & VINEY LTD., Aylesbury and Slough

PREFACE TO SECOND EDITION

WHEN this book first appeared in 1935, it was a decade or so before its time. Visual aids as such were not so designated, and the pedagogic approach to the theoretical side of even a scientific subject was still principally a literary approach. The era of the magic lantern had almost passed, and the era of the film strip, the ciné-projector, and other visual aids, had hardly arrived. But the visual approach, both at scholastic and academic levels, has now come into active practice; the needs of such an approach are recognised by the formation of such bodies as the National Foundation for Educational Research, the Committee for the Preparation of Visual Aids, and the Universities' Film Council.

Existing visual aids, such as films, charts, and collections of diagrams, have thus been brought to the fore, and no doubt much new material will be produced in the not too distant future.

In biological teaching, subjected as it must be to the seasonal availability of living specimens, charts and diagrams have perforce to be used, not of course as substitutes for living material, but as out-of-season supplements to the written book and the spoken word. The continued acceptance of this book, which can be advantageously owned by the student himself and conned at his leisure, is a welcome proof of its usefulness, and the issue of this new edition has accordingly made possible the correction of some minor errors in the labelling of the diagrams.

BLODWEN LLOYD.

1949.

PREFACE

THIS book contains a series of botanical sketches designed to illustrate a one-year lecture and laboratory course. It is based on diagrams which the author has for many years provided to students to facilitate teaching work both in the lecture-room and the laboratory. These appear to have met very adequately the needs of students both in school and college, so that the author has been prompted to revise them and have them issued in book form.

This collection of diagrams in its original form was prepared to cover the ground for the First Year University Examination and the Preliminary Scientific Examination of the Pharmaceutical Society. It has since been expanded, and while it has not been specifically prepared with a view to tutoring for any other examinations, it is suitable for such University curricula as the First Year Medical, Intermediate Science, and also for post-matriculation school work for the Higher Certificate. Part I (Morphology) and Part IV (Taxonomy of Phanerogams) may be used for pre-matriculation classes.

With the exception of a few sketches whose sources are acknowledged, the diagrams are original and prepared from actual specimens. The anatomical sketches are direct tracings made with the aid of a microprojector. Figs. 1-7, Pl. 61, have been made from preparations loaned by the Botany Department of the University, Glasgow.

In practice, the provision of a set of diagrams for each student has been found to have several advantages. In the lecture-room, the student may thus have before him some reasonably accurate illustrations of the lecture topic, thus compensating for his notoriously inaccurate and often unavoidably hasty copies of lantern slides or blackboard diagrams. Furthermore, in the laboratory, these diagrams may be used by the student as a ready source of reference for the naming of plant parts—with this proviso, that the copying into the student's laboratory notebook of anything not verified by his own observation is strongly to be deprecated. Finally, for the student working alone—particularly if he has only limited facilities for the necessary field work and laboratory practice, these diagrams appear to be a welcome supplement to the ordinary botanical text-book.

Grateful acknowledgment is here made to the author's colleague, Mr. J. A. Stewart, for revising the proofs of the diagrams and of the index.

BLODWEN LLOYD.

1935.

CONTENTS

8 CONTENTS

MORPHOLOGY OF PHANEROGAMS

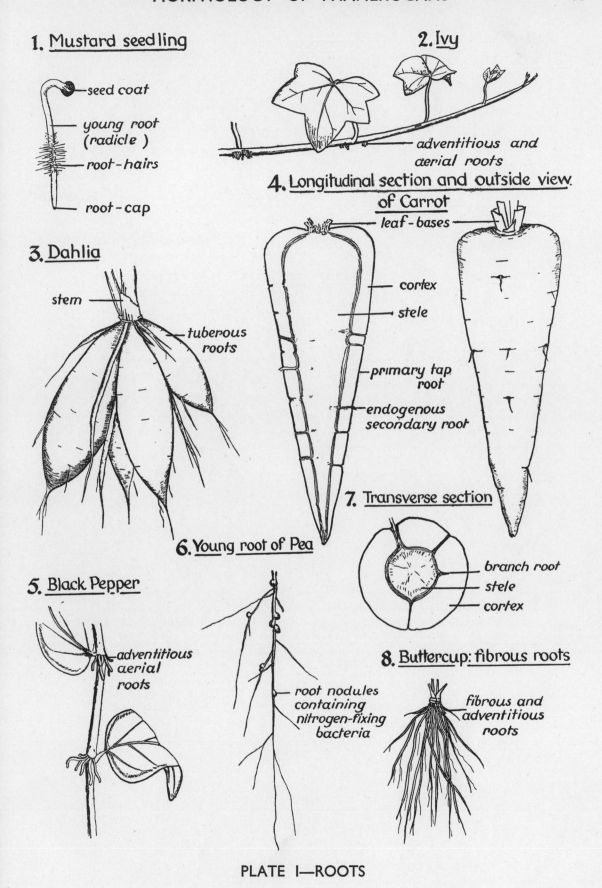

1. Mustard seedling
- seed coat
- young root (radicle)
- root-hairs
- root-cap

2. Ivy
- adventitious and aerial roots

3. Dahlia
- stem
- tuberous roots

4. Longitudinal section and outside view of Carrot
- leaf-bases
- cortex
- stele
- primary tap root
- endogenous secondary root

5. Black Pepper
- adventitious aerial roots

6. Young root of Pea
- root nodules containing nitrogen-fixing bacteria

7. Transverse section
- branch root
- stele
- cortex

8. Buttercup: fibrous roots
- fibrous and adventitious roots

PLATE I—ROOTS

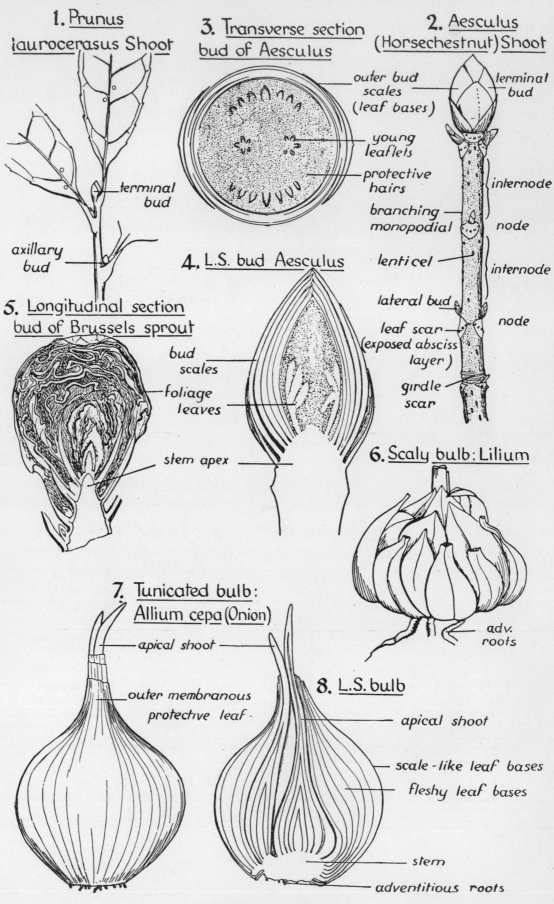

1. Prunus laurocerasus Shoot

terminal bud

axillary bud

3. Transverse section bud of Aesculus

outer bud scales (leaf bases)

young leaflets

protective hairs

2. Aesculus (Horsechestnut) Shoot

terminal bud

internode

branching monopodial

node

lenticel

internode

lateral bud

leaf scar (exposed absciss layer)

node

girdle scar

4. L.S. bud Aesculus

5. Longitudinal section bud of Brussels sprout

bud scales

foliage leaves

stem apex

6. Scaly bulb: Lilium

adv. roots

7. Tunicated bulb: Allium cepa (Onion)

apical shoot

outer membranous protective leaf

8. L.S. bulb

apical shoot

scale-like leaf bases

fleshy leaf bases

stem

adventitious roots

PLATE 2—STEMS

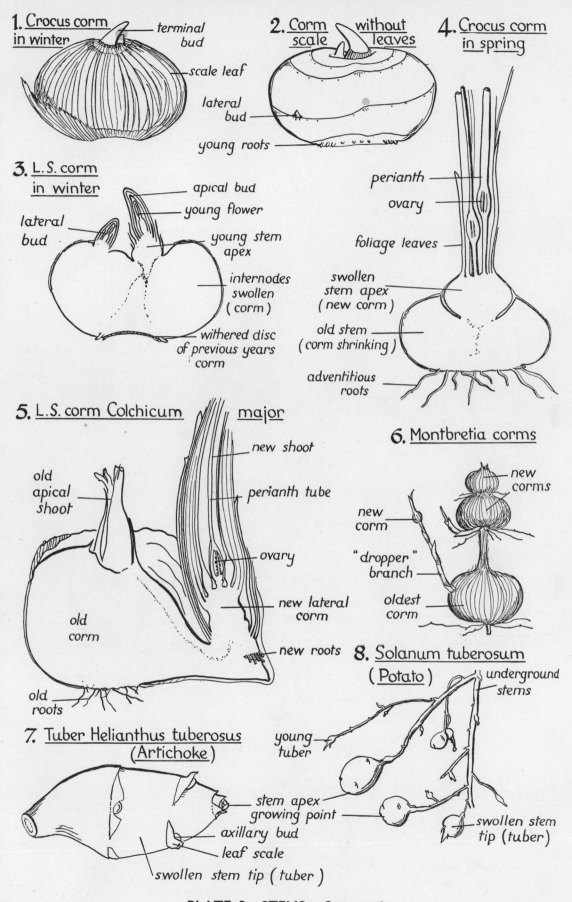

1. Crocus corm in winter — terminal bud, scale leaf, lateral bud, young roots

2. Corm scale without leaves

4. Crocus corm in spring — perianth, ovary, foliage leaves, swollen stem apex (new corm), old stem (corm shrinking), adventitious roots

3. L.S. corm in winter — apical bud, young flower, young stem apex, internodes swollen (corm), withered disc of previous years corm, lateral bud

5. L.S. corm Colchicum major — new shoot, perianth tube, ovary, new lateral corm, new roots, old apical shoot, old corm, old roots

6. Montbretia corms — new corms, new corm, "dropper" branch, oldest corm

8. Solanum tuberosum (Potato) — underground stems, young tuber, stem apex growing point, swollen stem tip (tuber)

7. Tuber Helianthus tuberosus (Artichoke) — stem apex growing point, axillary bud, leaf scale, swollen stem tip (tuber)

PLATE 3—STEMS—Continued

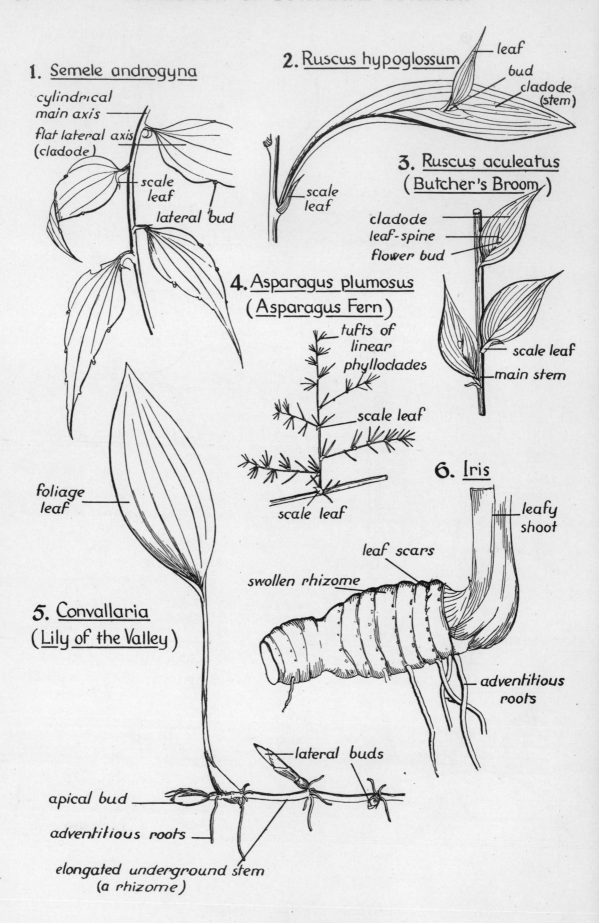

1. Semele androgyna

cylindrical main axis

flat lateral axis (cladode)

scale leaf

lateral bud

2. Ruscus hypoglossum

leaf

bud

cladode (stem)

scale leaf

3. Ruscus aculeatus (Butcher's Broom)

cladode

leaf-spine

flower bud

scale leaf

main stem

4. Asparagus plumosus (Asparagus Fern)

tufts of linear phylloclades

scale leaf

scale leaf

foliage leaf

6. Iris

leafy shoot

leaf scars

swollen rhizome

adventitious roots

5. Convallaria (Lily of the Valley)

lateral buds

apical bud

adventitious roots

elongated underground stem (a rhizome)

PLATE 4—STEMS—Continued

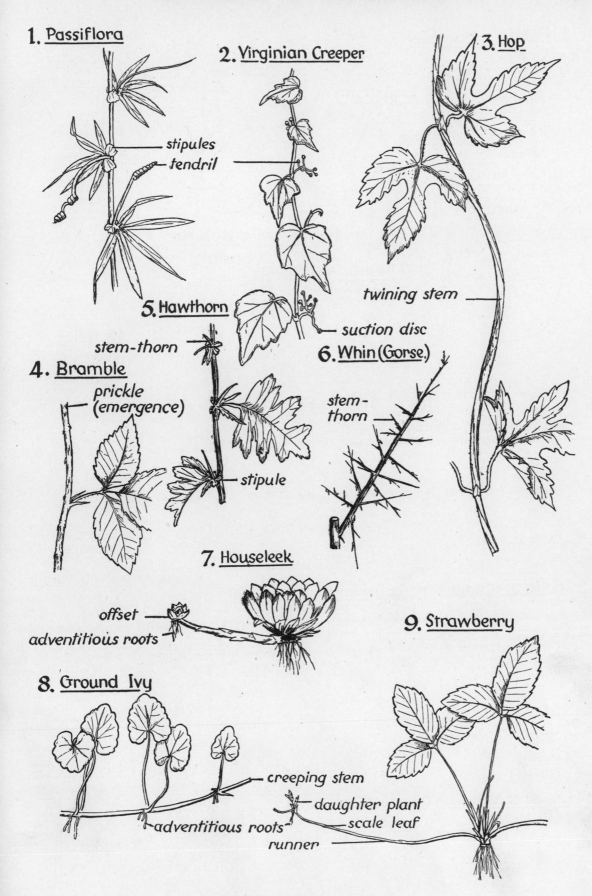

1. Passiflora

2. Virginian Creeper

3. Hop

stipules
tendril

5. Hawthorn

stem-thorn

4. Bramble
prickle
(emergence)

stipule

6. Whin (Gorse.)

stem-
thorn

suction disc

twining stem

7. Houseleek

offset
adventitious roots

9. Strawberry

8. Ground Ivy

creeping stem

daughter plant
scale leaf

adventitious roots

runner

PLATE 5—STEMS—Continued

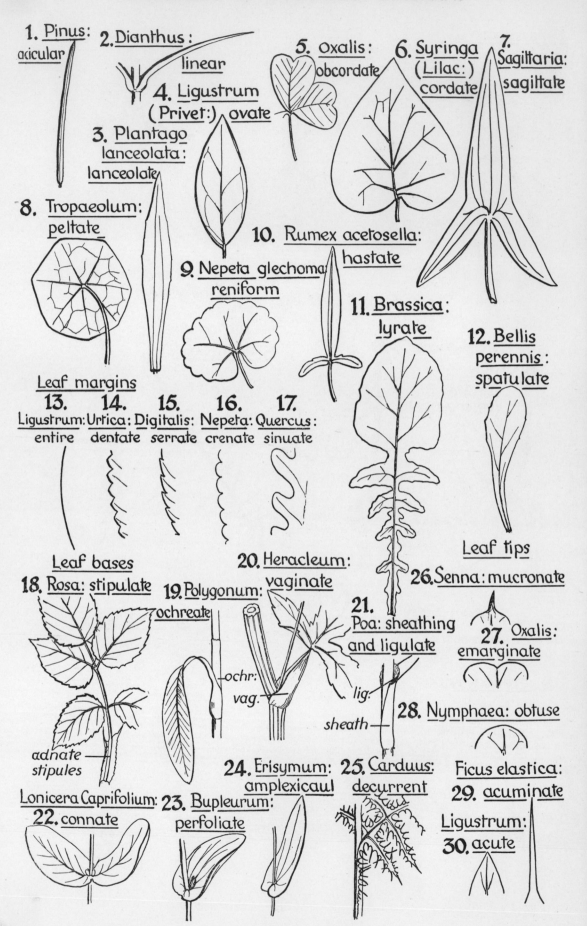

1. Pinus: acicular
2. Dianthus: linear
3. Plantago lanceolata: lanceolate
4. Ligustrum (Privet:) ovate
5. Oxalis: obcordate
6. Syringa (Lilac:) cordate
7. Sagittaria: sagittate
8. Tropaeolum: peltate
9. Nepeta glechoma reniform
10. Rumex acetosella: hastate
11. Brassica: lyrate
12. Bellis perennis: spatulate

Leaf margins
13. Ligustrum: entire
14. Urtica: dentate
15. Digitalis: serrate
16. Nepeta: crenate
17. Quercus: sinuate

Leaf bases
18. Rosa: stipulate
19. Polygonum: ochreate
20. Heracleum: vaginate
21. Poa: sheathing and ligulate
ochr:
vag:
lig.
sheath

Leaf tips
26. Senna: mucronate
27. Oxalis: emarginate
28. Nymphaea: obtuse
29. Ficus elastica: acuminate
30. Ligustrum: acute

adnate stipules
22. Lonicera Caprifolium: connate
23. Bupleurum: perfoliate
24. Erisymum: amplexicaul
25. Carduus: decurrent

PLATE 6—LEAVES

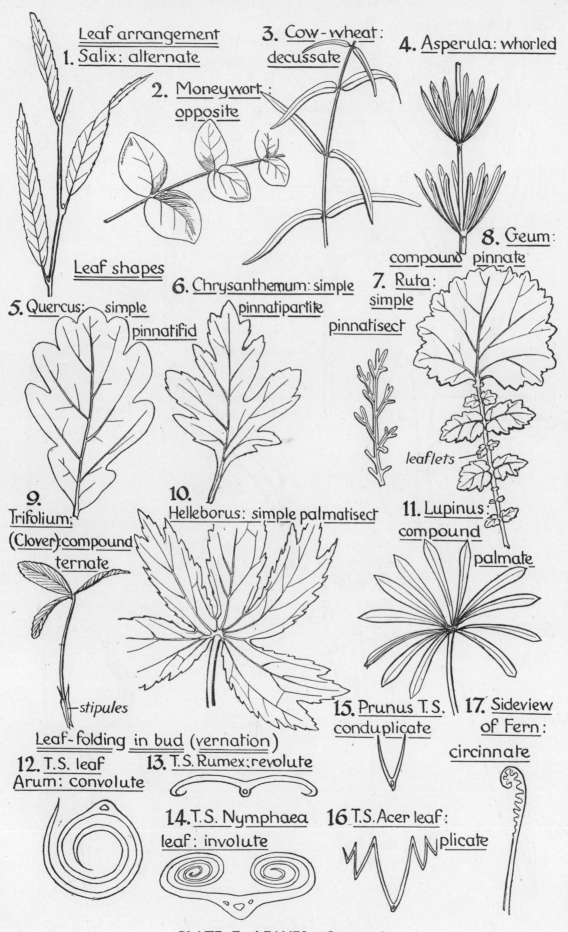

Leaf arrangement
1. Salix: alternate
2. Moneywort: opposite
3. Cow-wheat: decussate
4. Asperula: whorled

Leaf shapes
5. Quercus: simple pinnatifid
6. Chrysanthemum: simple pinnatipartite
7. Ruta: simple pinnatisect
8. Geum: compound pinnate
leaflets

9. Trifolium: (Clover) compound ternate
stipules
10. Helleborus: simple palmatisect
11. Lupinus: compound palmate

Leaf-folding in bud (vernation)
12. T.S. leaf Arum: convolute
13. T.S. Rumex: revolute
14. T.S. Nymphaea leaf: involute
15. Prunus T.S. conduplicate
16. T.S. Acer leaf: plicate
17. Sideview of Fern: circinnate

PLATE 7—LEAVES—*Continued*

B.D.—3

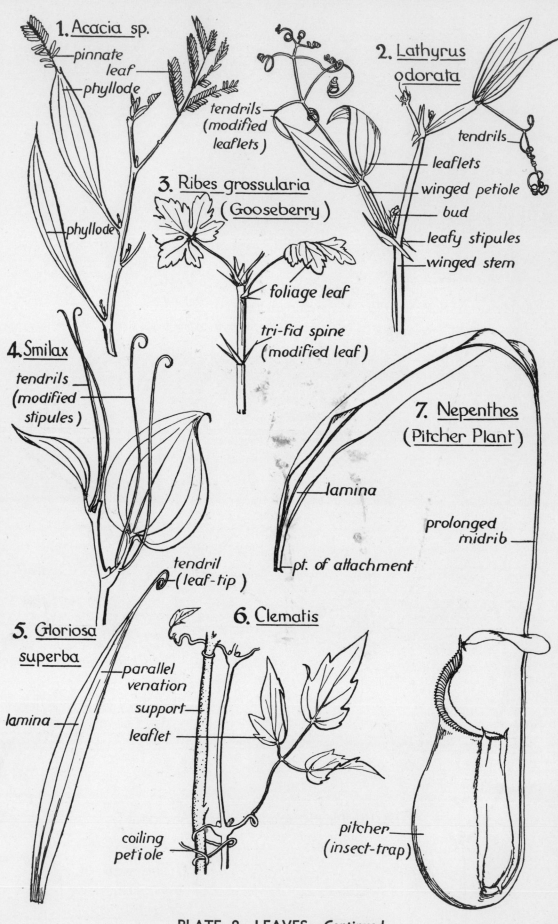

1. Acacia sp.
- pinnate leaf
- phyllode
- phyllode

2. Lathyrus odorata
- tendrils
- leaflets
- winged petiole
- bud
- leafy stipules
- winged stem

tendrils (modified leaflets)

3. Ribes grossularia (Gooseberry)
- foliage leaf
- tri-fid spine (modified leaf)

4. Smilax
- tendrils (modified stipules)

tendril (leaf-tip)

7. Nepenthes (Pitcher Plant)
- lamina
- pt. of attachment
- prolonged midrib

5. Gloriosa superba
- parallel venation
- lamina

6. Clematis
- support
- leaflet
- coiling petiole

pitcher (insect-trap)

PLATE 8—LEAVES—Continued

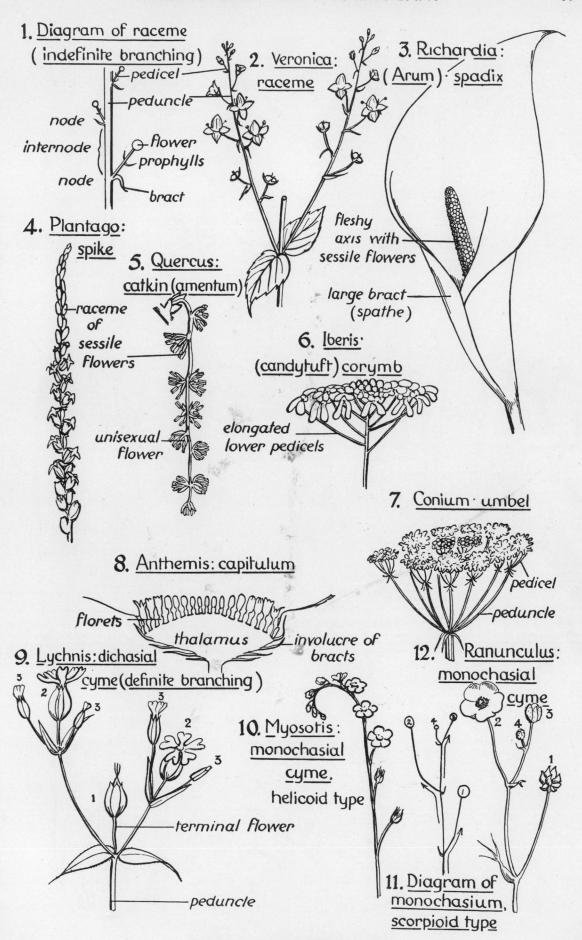

1. Diagram of raceme (indefinite branching)
   pedicel
   peduncle
   node
   internode
   node
   flower
   prophylls
   bract

2. Veronica: raceme

3. Richardia: (Arum): spadix
   fleshy axis with sessile flowers
   large bract (spathe)

4. Plantago: spike
   raceme of sessile flowers

5. Quercus: catkin (amentum)
   unisexual flower

6. Iberis: (candytuft) corymb
   elongated lower pedicels

7. Conium: umbel
   pedicel
   peduncle

8. Anthemis: capitulum
   florets
   thalamus
   involucre of bracts

9. Lychnis: dichasial cyme (definite branching)
   terminal flower
   peduncle

10. Myosotis: monochasial cyme, helicoid type

11. Diagram of monochasium, scorpioid type

12. Ranunculus: monochasial cyme

PLATE 9—INFLORESCENCES

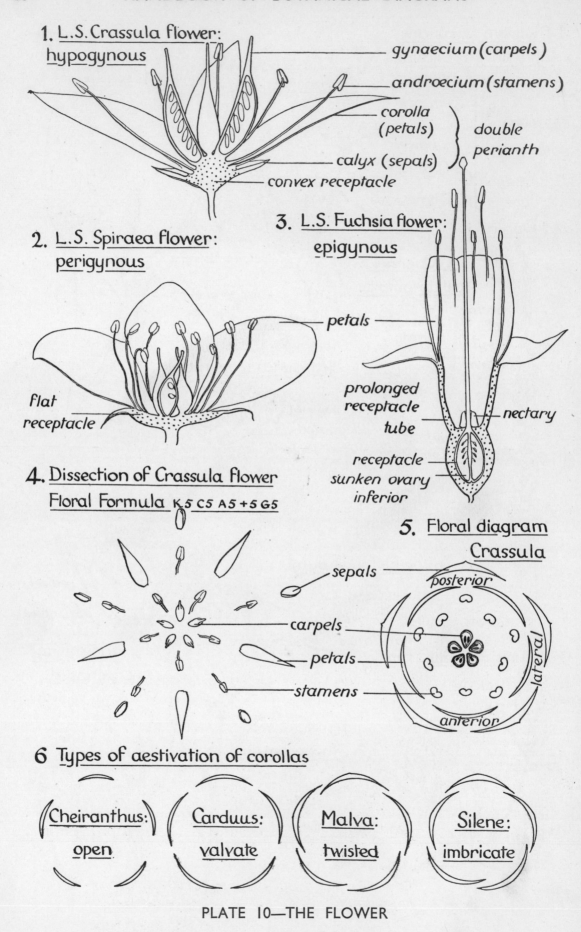

1. L.S. Crassula flower: hypogynous

gynaecium (carpels)

androecium (stamens)

corolla (petals)

calyx (sepals) } double perianth

convex receptacle

2. L.S. Spiraea flower: perigynous

3. L.S. Fuchsia flower: epigynous

petals

flat receptacle

prolonged receptacle tube

nectary

receptacle sunken ovary inferior

4. Dissection of Crassula flower
Floral Formula K5 C5 A5+5 G5

sepals

carpels

petals

stamens

5. Floral diagram Crassula

posterior

lateral

anterior

6 Types of aestivation of corollas

Cheiranthus: open

Carduus: valvate

Malva: twisted

Silene: imbricate

PLATE 10—THE FLOWER

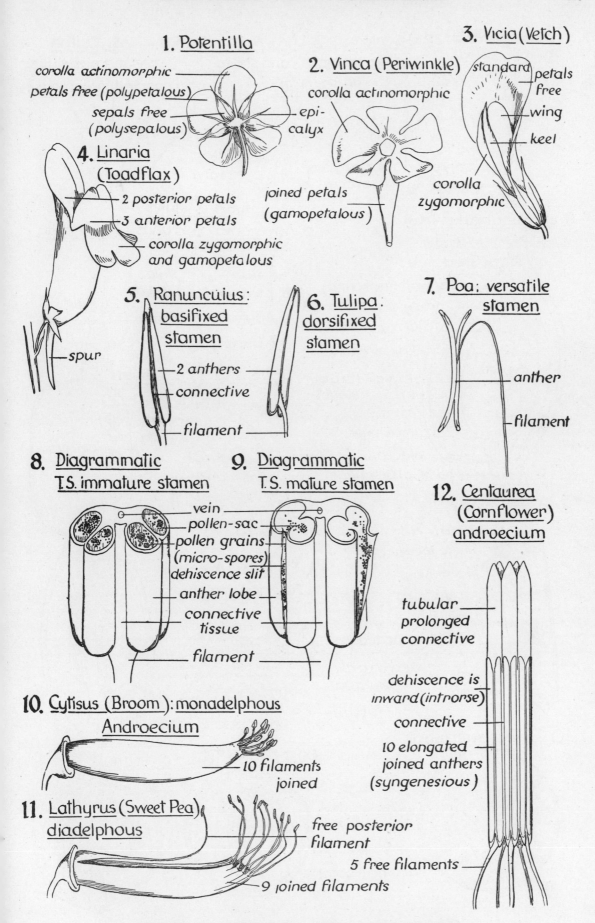

1. Potentilla

corolla actinomorphic

petals free (polypetalous)

sepals free (polysepalous)

epi-calyx

2. Vinca (Periwinkle)

corolla actinomorphic

joined petals (gamopetalous)

3. Vicia (Vetch)

standard

petals free

wing

keel

corolla zygomorphic

4. Linaria (Toadflax)

2 posterior petals

3 anterior petals

corolla zygomorphic and gamopetalous

spur

5. Ranunculus: basifixed stamen

2 anthers

connective

filament

6. Tulipa: dorsifixed stamen

7. Poa: versatile stamen

anther

filament

8. Diagrammatic T.S. immature stamen

vein

pollen-sac

pollen grains (micro-spores)

dehiscence slit

anther lobe

connective tissue

filament

9. Diagrammatic T.S. mature stamen

12. Centaurea (Cornflower) androecium

tubular prolonged connective

dehiscence is inward (introrse)

connective

10 elongated joined anthers (syngenesious)

10. Cytisus (Broom): monadelphous Androecium

10 filaments joined

11. Lathyrus (Sweet Pea) diadelphous

free posterior filament

5 free filaments

9 joined filaments

PLATE II—PERIANTH AND ANDRŒCIUM

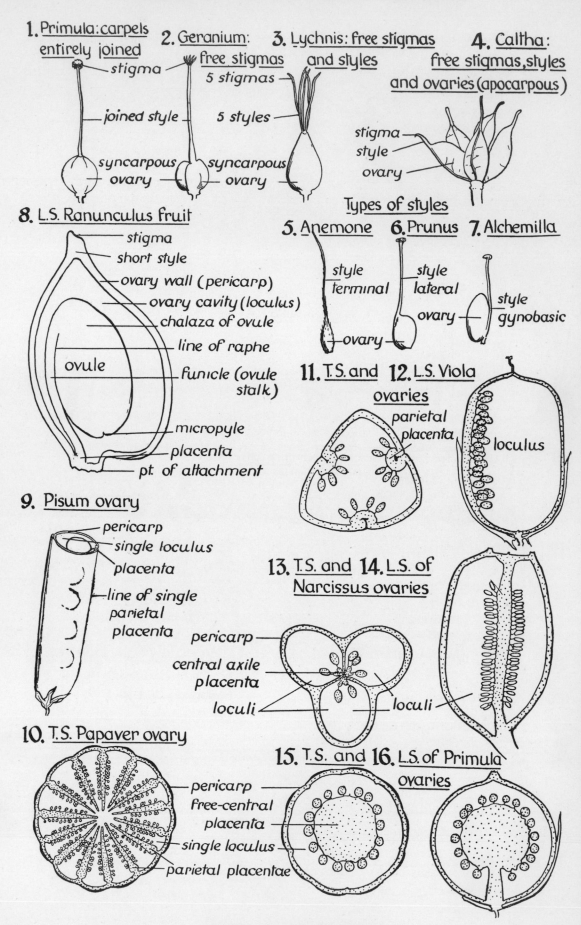

1. Primula: carpels entirely joined
— stigma
joined style
syncarpous ovary

2. Geranium: free stigmas
5 stigmas
5 styles
syncarpous ovary

3. Lychnis: free stigmas and styles

4. Caltha: free stigmas, styles and ovaries (apocarpous)
stigma
style
ovary

8. L.S. Ranunculus fruit
— stigma
— short style
— ovary wall (pericarp)
— ovary cavity (loculus)
— chalaza of ovule
— line of raphe
ovule
— funicle (ovule stalk)
— micropyle
— placenta
— pt. of attachment

Types of styles
5. Anemone   6. Prunus   7. Alchemilla
style terminal
ovary
style lateral
ovary
style gynobasic

9. Pisum ovary
— pericarp
— single loculus
— placenta
— line of single parietal placenta

11. T.S. and   12. L.S. Viola ovaries
parietal placenta
loculus

13. T.S. and   14. L.S. of Narcissus ovaries
pericarp
central axile placenta
loculi
loculi

10. T.S. Papaver ovary
— pericarp
— free-central placenta
— single loculus
— parietal placentae

15. T.S. and   16. L.S. of Primula ovaries

PLATE 12—GYNÆCIUM

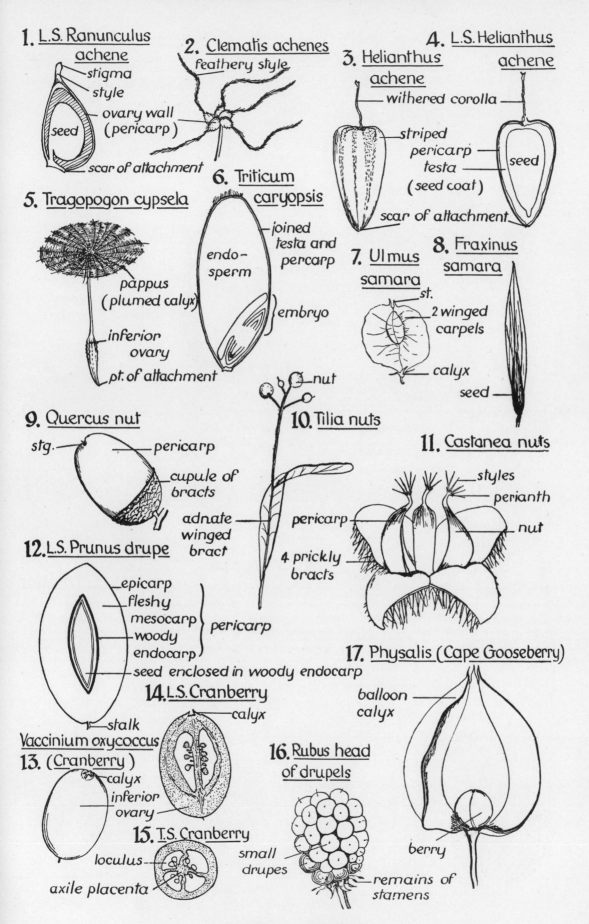

1. L.S. Ranunculus achene
— stigma
— style
— ovary wall (pericarp)
seed
— scar of attachment

2. Clematis achenes feathery style

3. Helianthus achene
— withered corolla —
— striped pericarp
testa (seed coat)
scar of attachment

4. L.S. Helianthus achene
seed

5. Tragopogon cypsela
pappus (plumed calyx)
inferior ovary
pt. of attachment

6. Triticum caryopsis
— joined testa and percarp
endo-sperm
— embryo

7. Ulmus samara
st.
2 winged carpels
calyx

8. Fraxinus samara
seed

9. Quercus nut
stg.
— pericarp
— cupule of bracts

10. Tilia nuts
nut
adnate winged bract
pericarp
4 prickly bracts

11. Castanea nuts
styles
perianth
nut

12. L.S. Prunus drupe
epicarp
fleshy
mesocarp
woody
endocarp
pericarp
— seed enclosed in woody endocarp
— stalk

Vaccinium oxycoccus
13. (Cranberry)
calyx
inferior ovary

14. L.S. Cranberry
calyx

15. T.S. Cranberry
loculus
axile placenta

16. Rubus head of drupels
small drupes

17. Physalis (Cape Gooseberry)
balloon calyx
berry
remains of stamens

PLATE 13—FRUITS

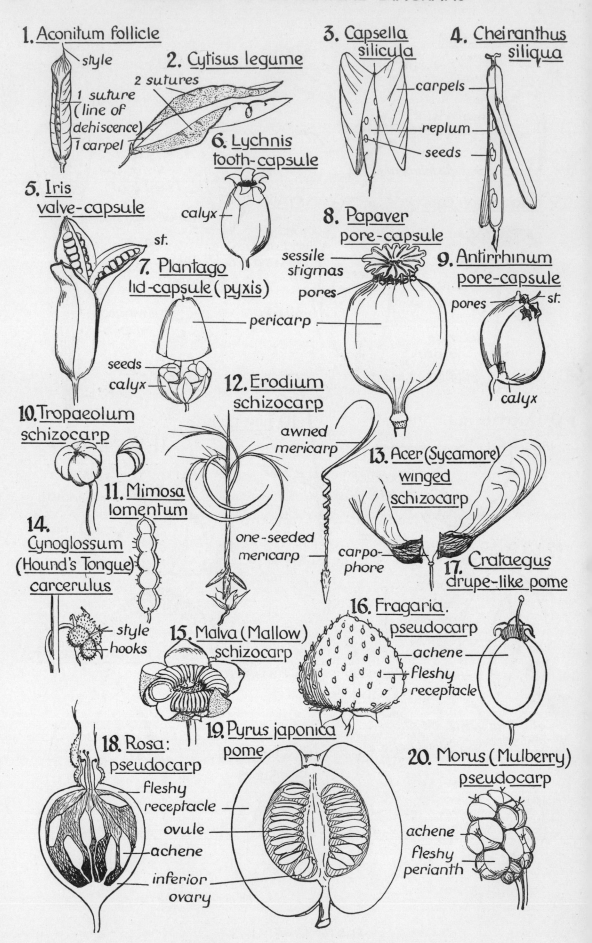

1. Aconitum follicle
  style
  1 suture (line of dehiscence)
  1 carpel

2. Cytisus legume
  2 sutures

3. Capsella silicula
  carpels
  replum
  seeds

4. Cheiranthus siliqua

5. Iris valve-capsule
  st.

6. Lychnis tooth-capsule
  calyx

7. Plantago lid-capsule (pyxis)
  pericarp
  seeds
  calyx

8. Papaver pore-capsule
  sessile stigmas
  pores

9. Antirrhinum pore-capsule
  pores
  st.
  calyx

10. Tropaeolum schizocarp

11. Mimosa lomentum

12. Erodium schizocarp
  awned mericarp
  one-seeded mericarp
  carpo-phore

13. Acer (Sycamore) winged schizocarp

14. Cynoglossum (Hound's Tongue) carcerulus
  style
  hooks

15. Malva (Mallow) schizocarp

16. Fragaria. pseudocarp
  achene
  fleshy receptacle

17. Crataegus drupe-like pome

18. Rosa: pseudocarp
  fleshy receptacle
  ovule
  achene
  inferior ovary

19. Pyrus japonica pome

20. Morus (Mulberry) pseudocarp
  achene
  fleshy perianth

PLATE 14—FRUITS—Continued

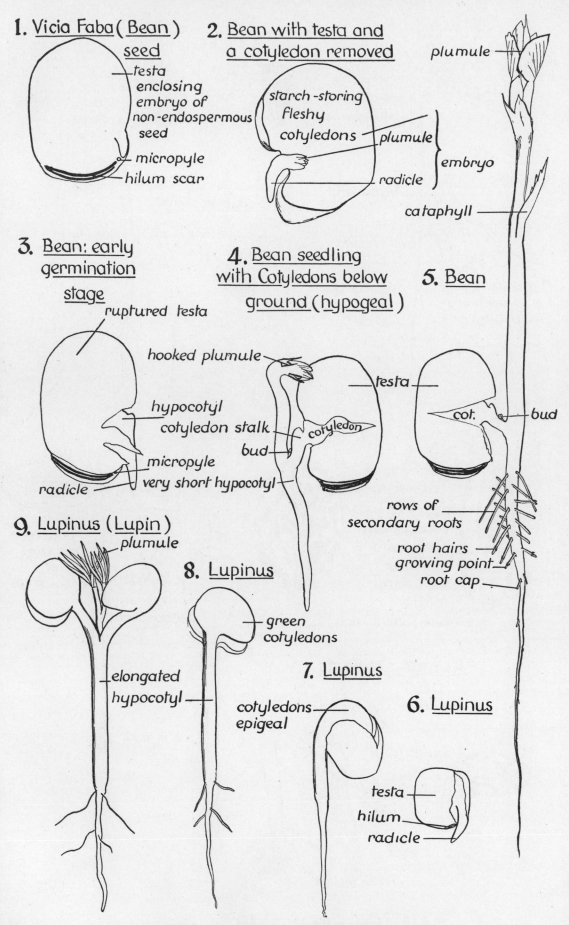

1. Vicia Faba (Bean) seed
testa enclosing embryo of non-endospermous seed
micropyle
hilum scar

2. Bean with testa and a cotyledon removed
starch-storing fleshy cotyledons
plumule
radicle
embryo

plumule
cataphyll

3. Bean: early germination stage
ruptured testa
hypocotyl
cotyledon stalk
bud
micropyle
very short hypocotyl
radicle

4. Bean seedling with Cotyledons below ground (hypogeal)
hooked plumule
cotyledon
bud

5. Bean
testa
cot.
bud

rows of secondary roots
root hairs
growing point
root cap

9. Lupinus (Lupin)
plumule
elongated hypocotyl

8. Lupinus
green cotyledons

7. Lupinus
cotyledons epigeal

6. Lupinus
testa
hilum
radicle

PLATE 15—SEEDS AND SEEDLINGS

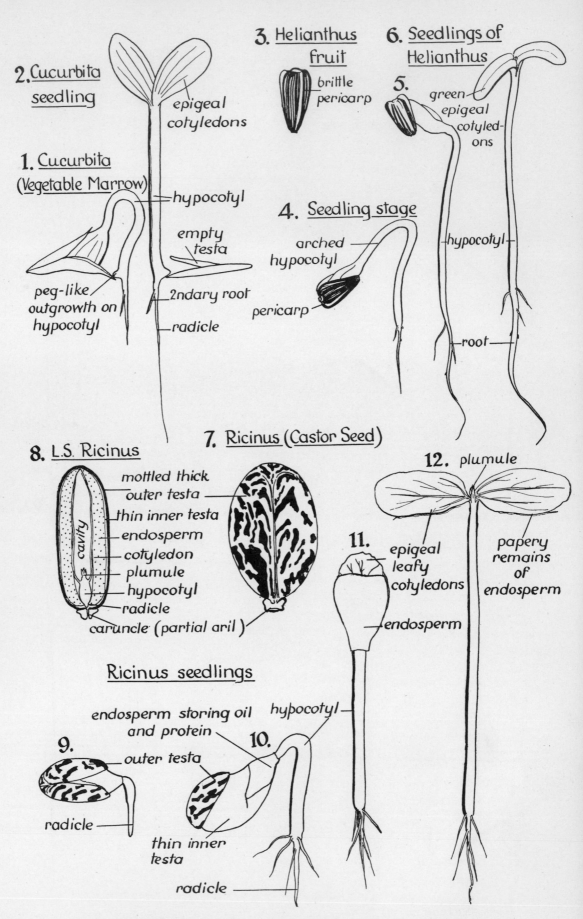

2. Cucurbita seedling

epigeal cotyledons

1. Cucurbita (Vegetable Marrow)

hypocotyl

empty testa

peg-like outgrowth on hypocotyl

2ndary root

radicle

3. Helianthus fruit

brittle pericarp

4. Seedling stage

arched hypocotyl

pericarp

6. Seedlings of Helianthus

5.

green epigeal cotyled-ons

hypocotyl

root

8. L.S. Ricinus

mottled thick outer testa

thin inner testa

endosperm

cotyledon

plumule

hypocotyl

radicle

caruncle (partial aril)

cavity

7. Ricinus (Castor Seed)

12. plumule

papery remains of endosperm

11.

epigeal leafy cotyledons

endosperm

Ricinus seedlings

endosperm storing oil and protein

outer testa

hypocotyl

9.

radicle

10.

thin inner testa

radicle

PLATE 16—SEEDS AND SEEDLINGS—*Continued*

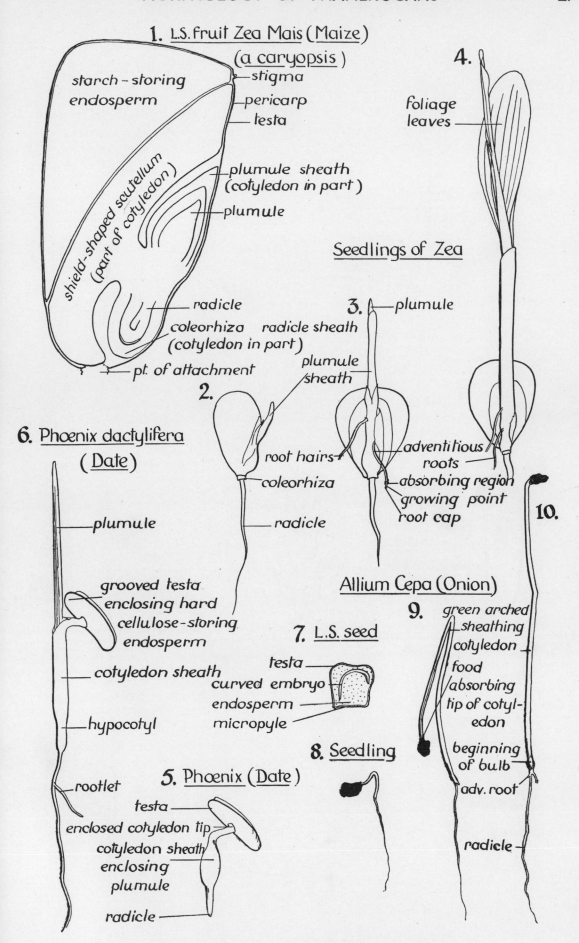

1. L.S. fruit Zea Mais (Maize)

(a caryopsis)

starch - storing endosperm

stigma

pericarp

testa

shield-shaped scutellum (part of cotyledon)

plumule sheath (cotyledon in part)

plumule

radicle

coleorhiza (cotyledon in part)

pt. of attachment

4.

foliage leaves

Seedlings of Zea

3. plumule

radicle sheath

plumule sheath

root hairs

coleorhiza

radicle

2.

adventitious roots

absorbing region

growing point

root cap

10.

6. Phoenix dactylifera (Date)

plumule

grooved testa enclosing hard cellulose-storing endosperm

cotyledon sheath

hypocotyl

rootlet

5. Phoenix (Date)

testa

enclosed cotyledon tip

cotyledon sheath enclosing plumule

radicle

7. L.S. seed

testa

curved embryo

endosperm

micropyle

8. Seedling

Allium Cepa (Onion)

9. green arched sheathing cotyledon

food absorbing tip of cotyledon

beginning of bulb

adv. root

radicle

PLATE 17—SEEDS AND SEEDLINGS—*Continued*

ANATOMY OF PHANEROGAMS

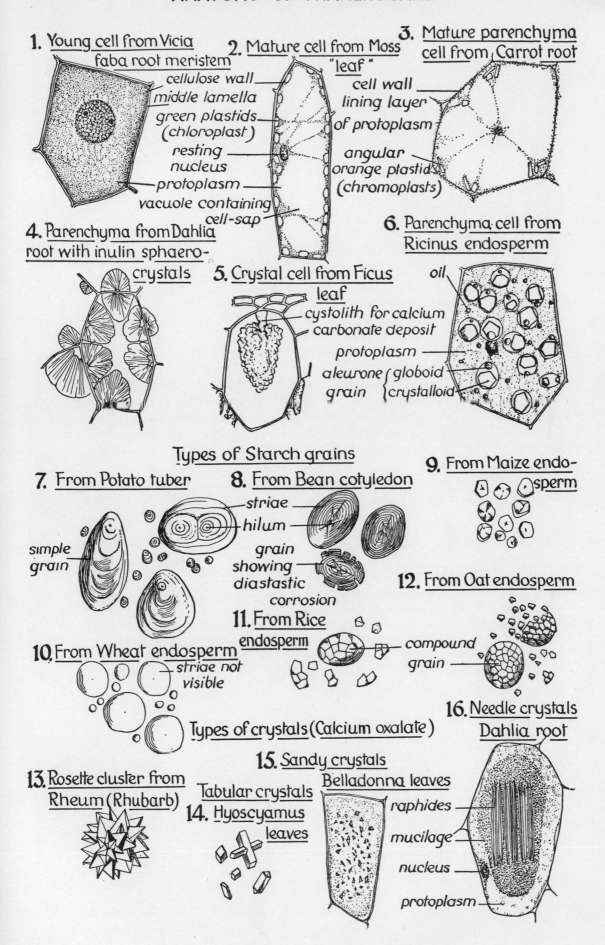

1. Young cell from Vicia faba root meristem
cellulose wall
middle lamella
green plastids (chloroplast)
resting nucleus
protoplasm
vacuole containing cell-sap

2. Mature cell from Moss "leaf"
cell wall
lining layer of protoplasm
angular orange plastid (chromoplasts)

3. Mature parenchyma cell from Carrot root

4. Parenchyma from Dahlia root with inulin sphaero-crystals

5. Crystal cell from Ficus leaf
cystolith for calcium carbonate deposit
protoplasm
aleurone grain { globoid / crystalloid

6. Parenchyma cell from Ricinus endosperm
oil

Types of Starch grains

7. From Potato tuber
simple grain

8. From Bean cotyledon
striae
hilum
grain showing diastastic corrosion

9. From Maize endosperm

10. From Wheat endosperm
striae not visible

11. From Rice endosperm

12. From Oat endosperm
compound grain

Types of crystals (Calcium oxalate)

13. Rosette cluster from Rheum (Rhubarb)

14. Hyoscyamus leaves
Tabular crystals

15. Sandy crystals Belladonna leaves

16. Needle crystals Dahlia root
raphides
mucilage
nucleus
protoplasm

PLATE 18—CELLS AND CELL CONTENTS

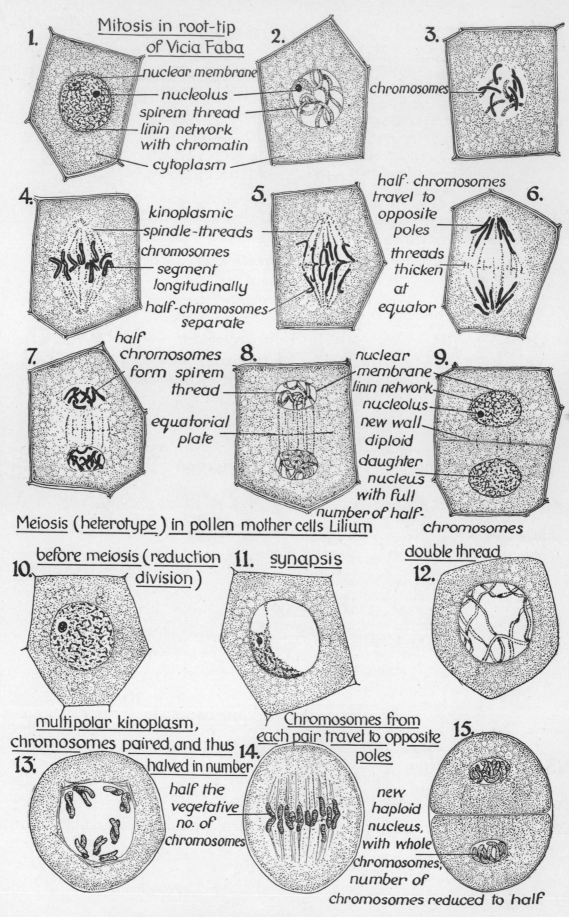

1. Mitosis in root-tip of Vicia Faba

nuclear membrane
nucleolus
spirem thread
linin network with chromatin
cytoplasm

2.

3. chromosomes

4. kinoplasmic spindle-threads
chromosomes
segment longitudinally
half-chromosomes separate

5.

half chromosomes travel to opposite poles

threads thicken at equator

6.

7. half chromosomes form spirem thread

equatorial plate

8.

nuclear membrane
linin network
nucleolus
new wall
diploid daughter nucleus with full number of half-chromosomes

9.

Meiosis (heterotype) in pollen mother cells Lilium

10. before meiosis (reduction division)

11. synapsis

12. double thread

multipolar kinoplasm, chromosomes paired, and thus halved in number

13.

14. Chromosomes from each pair travel to opposite poles

half the vegetative no. of chromosomes

15. new haploid nucleus, with whole chromosomes; number of chromosomes reduced to half

PLATE 19—NUCLEAR DIVISION : KARYOKINESIS

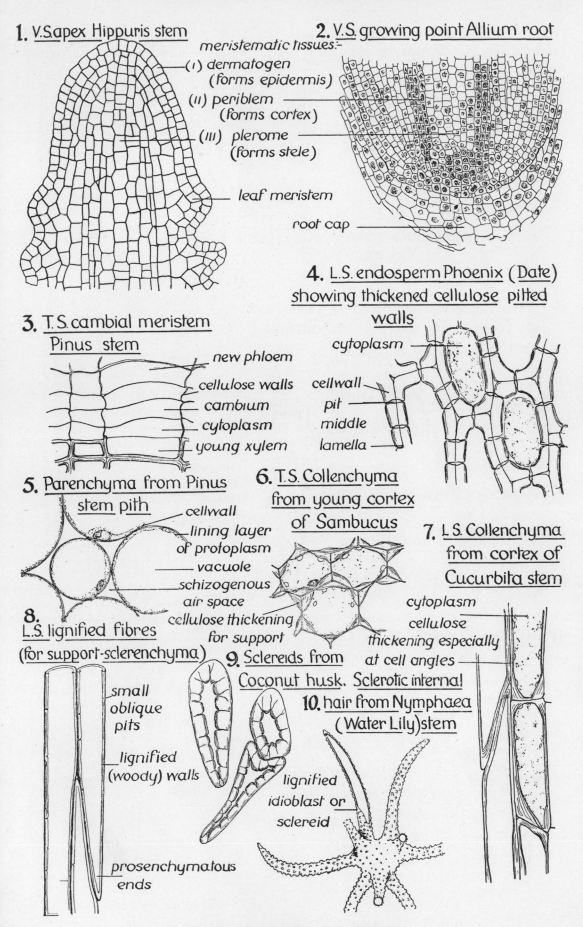

1. V.S. apex Hippuris stem

2. V.S. growing point Allium root

meristematic tissues:-
- (I) dermatogen (forms epidermis)
- (II) periblem (forms cortex)
- (III) plerome (forms stele)

leaf meristem

root cap

4. L.S. endosperm Phoenix (Date) showing thickened cellulose pitted walls

cytoplasm

cellwall
pit
middle
lamella

3. T.S. cambial meristem Pinus stem

new phloem
cellulose walls
cambium
cytoplasm
young xylem

5. Parenchyma from Pinus stem pith

cellwall
lining layer of protoplasm
vacuole
schizogenous air space
cellulose thickening for support

6. T.S. Collenchyma from young cortex of Sambucus

7. L.S. Collenchyma from cortex of Cucurbita stem

cytoplasm
cellulose thickening especially at cell angles

8. L.S. lignified fibres (for support-sclerenchyma)

small oblique pits

lignified (woody) walls

prosenchymatous ends

9. Sclereids from Coconut husk. Sclerotic internal

10. hair from Nymphaea (Water Lily) stem

lignified idioblast or sclereid

PLATE 20—TYPES OF TISSUES

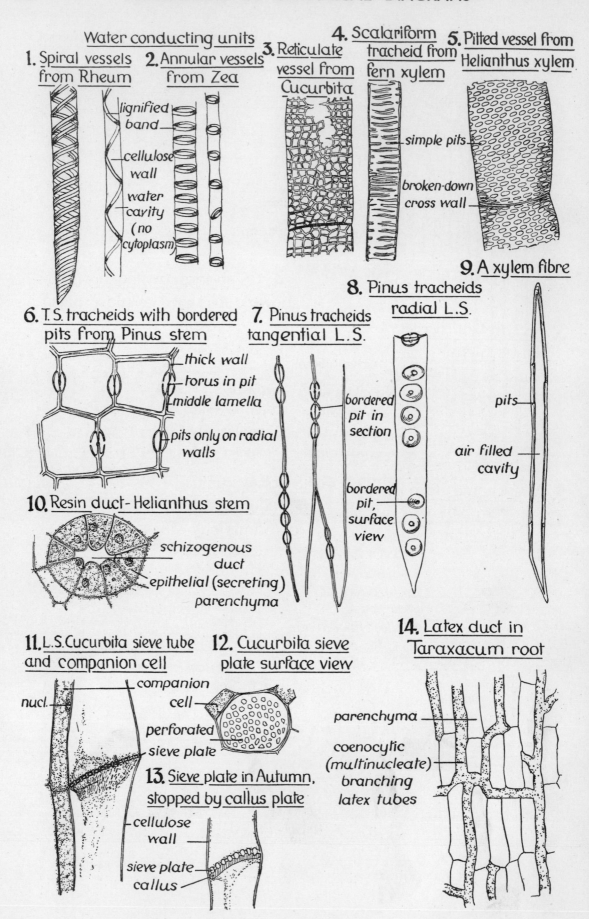

Water conducting units

1. Spiral vessels from Rheum

2. Annular vessels from Zea

lignified band

cellulose wall

water cavity (no cytoplasm)

3. Reticulate vessel from Cucurbita

4. Scalariform tracheid from fern xylem

5. Pitted vessel from Helianthus xylem

simple pits

broken-down cross wall

6. T.S. tracheids with bordered pits from Pinus stem

thick wall

torus in pit

middle lamella

pits only on radial walls

7. Pinus tracheids tangential L.S.

8. Pinus tracheids radial L.S.

bordered pit in section

bordered pit, surface view

9. A xylem fibre

pits

air filled cavity

10. Resin duct-Helianthus stem

schizogenous duct

epithelial (secreting) parenchyma

11. L.S.Cucurbita sieve tube and companion cell

nucl.

companion cell

perforated sieve plate

12. Cucurbita sieve plate surface view

13. Sieve plate in Autumn, stopped by callus plate

cellulose wall

sieve plate callus

14. Latex duct in Taraxacum root

parenchyma

coenocytic (multinucleate) branching latex tubes

PLATE 21—TYPES OF CONDUCTING TISSUES

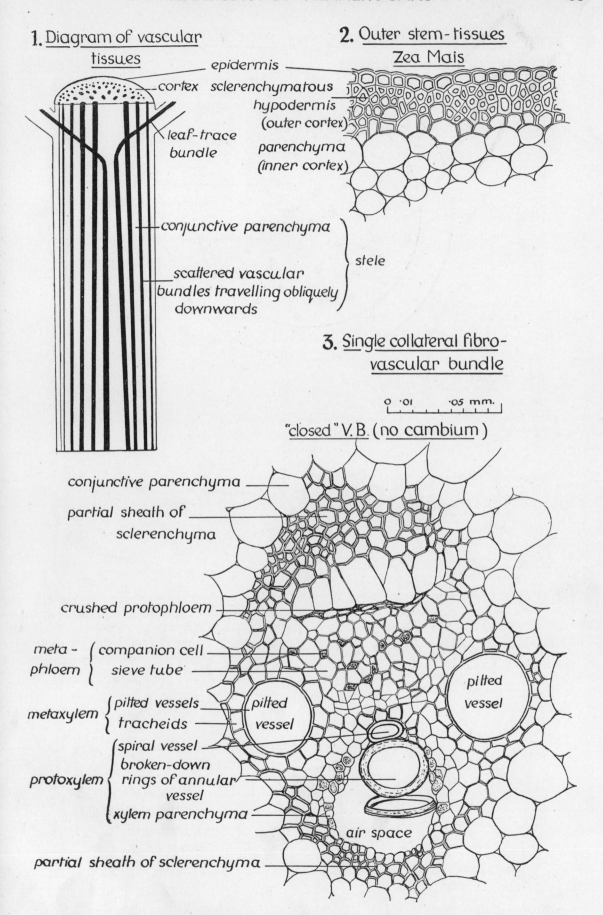

1. Diagram of vascular tissues

epidermis
cortex
leaf-trace bundle
conjunctive parenchyma
scattered vascular bundles travelling obliquely downwards
stele

2. Outer stem-tissues Zea Mais

epidermis
sclerenchymatous hypodermis (outer cortex)
parenchyma (inner cortex)

3. Single collateral fibro-vascular bundle

0   ·01   ·05 mm.

"closed" V.B. (no cambium)

conjunctive parenchyma
partial sheath of sclerenchyma
crushed protophloem
meta- { companion cell
phloem { sieve tube
metaxylem { pitted vessels
{ tracheids
{ spiral vessel
{ broken-down
protoxylem { rings of annular vessel
{ xylem parenchyma
partial sheath of sclerenchyma

pitted vessel
pitted vessel
air space

PLATE 22—MONOCOTYLEDONOUS STEM: ZEA MAIS

1. <u>Diagram showing tissue arrangement as seen in transverse section</u>
<u>Vanilla planifolia</u> (climber)

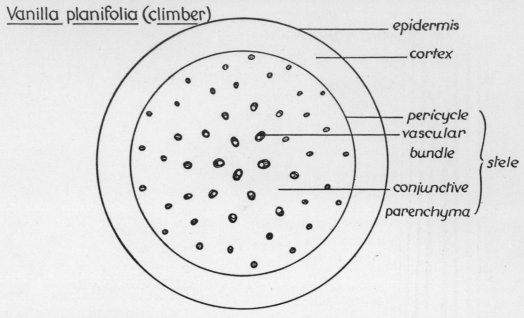

- epidermis
- cortex
- pericycle
- vascular bundle
- conjunctive parenchyma
} stele

2. <u>T.S. single V.B.</u>

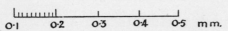

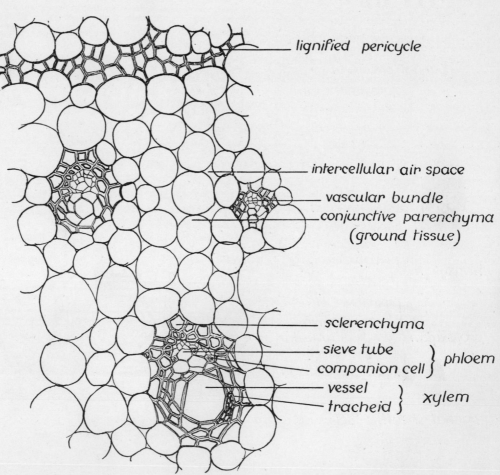

- lignified pericycle
- intercellular air space
- vascular bundle
- conjunctive parenchyma (ground tissue)
- sclerenchyma
- sieve tube
- companion cell } phloem
- vessel
- tracheid } xylem

PLATE 23—MONOCOTYLEDONOUS STEM : VANILLA

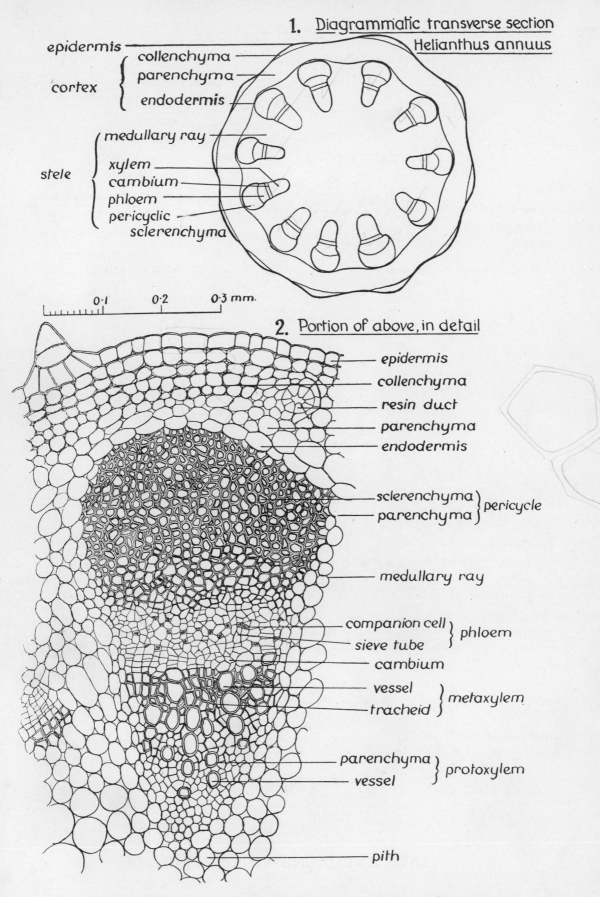

1. <u>Diagrammatic transverse section</u>
<u>Helianthus annuus</u>

epidermis

cortex {
collenchyma
parenchyma
endodermis
}

stele {
medullary ray
xylem
cambium
phloem
pericyclic
sclerenchyma
}

0.1   0.2   0.3 mm.

2. <u>Portion of above, in detail</u>

epidermis
collenchyma
resin duct
parenchyma
endodermis

sclerenchyma } pericycle
parenchyma

medullary ray

companion cell } phloem
sieve tube
cambium
vessel } metaxylem
tracheid

parenchyma } protoxylem
vessel

pith

PLATE 24—YOUNG DICOTYLEDONOUS STEM : HELIANTHUS

T.S. portion of stem Cucurbita (climber)

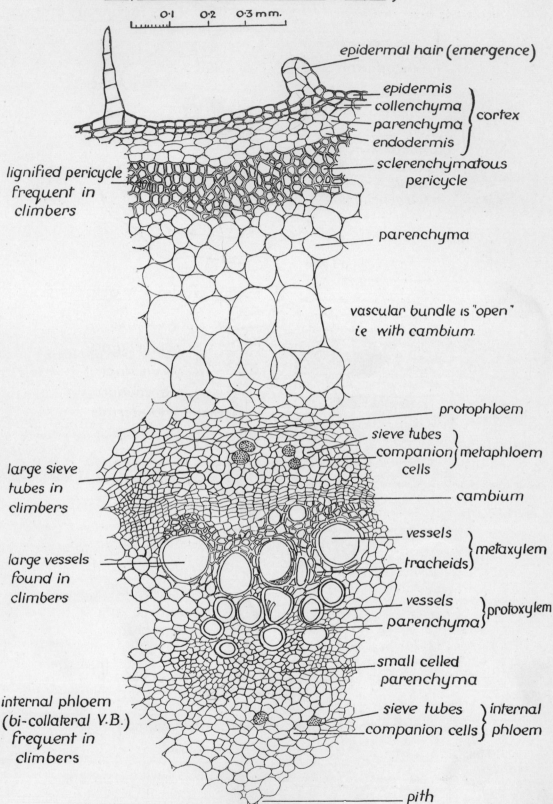

PLATE 25—CLIMBING STEM : CUCURBITA

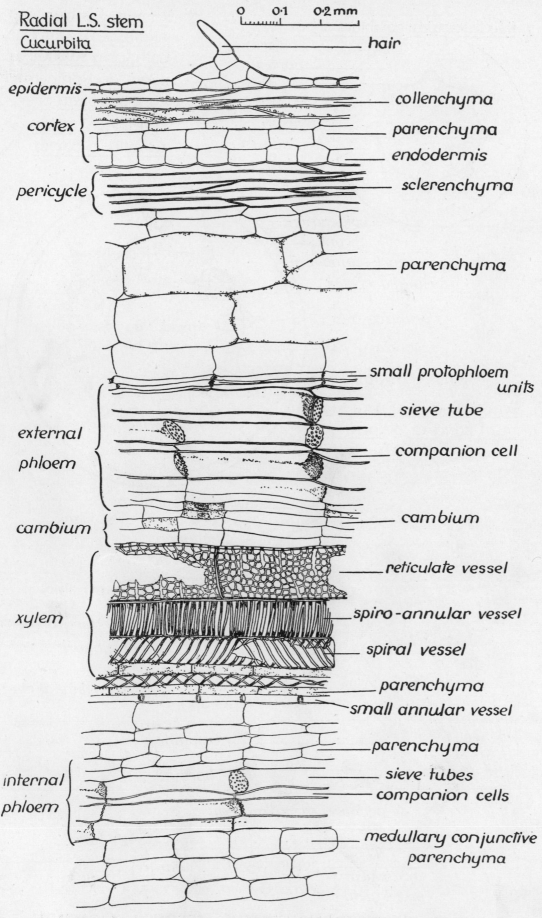

Radial L.S. stem
Cucurbita

0   0·1   0·2 mm

hair

epidermis

cortex
- collenchyma
- parenchyma
- endodermis

pericycle
- sclerenchyma

parenchyma

small protophloem
units
sieve tube

external
phloem
companion cell

cambium
cambium

reticulate vessel

xylem
spiro-annular vessel

spiral vessel

parenchyma
small annular vessel

parenchyma

internal
phloem
sieve tubes
companion cells

medullary conjunctive
parenchyma

PLATE 26—CLIMBING STEM : CUCURBITA—*Continued*

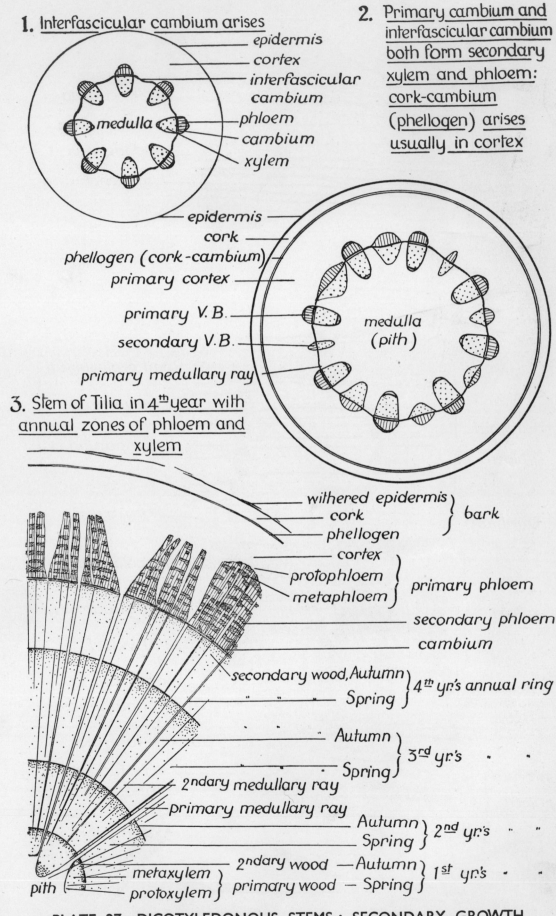

1. Interfascicular cambium arises

- epidermis
- cortex
- interfascicular cambium
- phloem
- cambium
- xylem

medulla

2. Primary cambium and interfascicular cambium both form secondary xylem and phloem: cork-cambium (phellogen) arises usually in cortex

- epidermis
- cork
- phellogen (cork-cambium)
- primary cortex
- primary V.B.
- secondary V.B.
- primary medullary ray

medulla (pith)

3. Stem of Tilia in 4ᵗʰ year with annual zones of phloem and xylem

- withered epidermis ⎫
- cork ⎬ bark
- phellogen ⎭
- cortex
- protophloem ⎫ primary phloem
- metaphloem ⎭
- secondary phloem
- cambium
- secondary wood, Autumn ⎫ 4ᵗʰ yr's annual ring
-    "   "   Spring ⎭
- "   Autumn ⎫ 3ʳᵈ yr's
- "   Spring ⎭
- 2ⁿᵈary medullary ray
- primary medullary ray
- Autumn ⎫ 2ⁿᵈ yr's
- Spring ⎭
- 2ⁿᵈary wood — Autumn ⎫ 1ˢᵗ yr's
- primary wood — Spring ⎭

metaxylem ⎫
protoxylem ⎭
pith

PLATE 27—DICOTYLEDONOUS STEMS : SECONDARY GROWTH

1. <u>T.S. lenticel Sambucus</u>

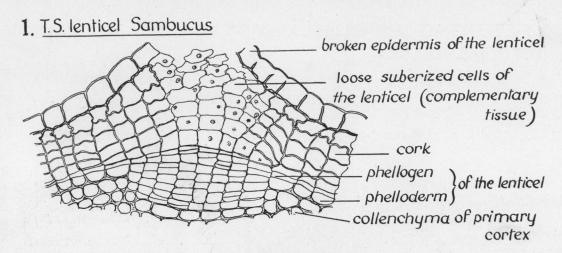

— broken epidermis of the lenticel

— loose *suberized cells of the lenticel (complementary tissue)*

— cork

— phellogen } of the lenticel

— phelloderm }

— collenchyma of primary cortex

2. <u>T.S. Sambucus (Elder) stem. 1 year old</u>

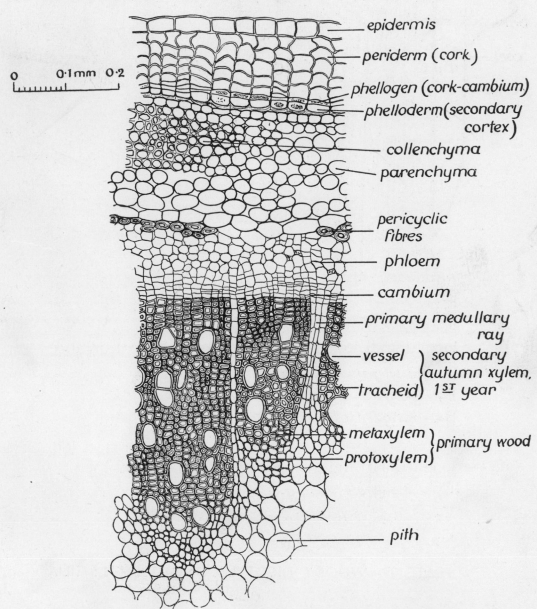

0   0·1mm 0·2

— epidermis

— periderm (cork)

— phellogen (cork-cambium)

— phelloderm (secondary cortex)

— collenchyma

— parenchyma

— pericyclic fibres

— phloem

— cambium

— primary medullary ray

— vessel } secondary autumn xylem, 1ST year

— tracheid }

— metaxylem } primary wood

— protoxylem }

— pith

PLATE 28—WOODY DICOTYLEDONOUS STEM : SAMBUCUS

Diagrammatic representation of Tilia (Lime)
twig in its fourth year

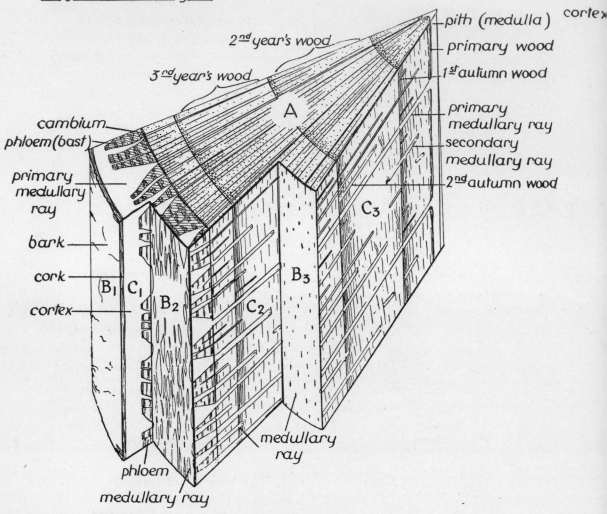

A — transverse view, showing all tissues
B — longitudinal tangential views, parallel to one another
   B₁ – external view showing bark
   B₂ – tangential section through bast
   B₃ – tangential section through wood

C — longitudinal radial views, parallel to one another
   C₁ – shows cortex and outer bast
   C₂ – " inner bast, cambium and wood
   C₃ – " wood and pith

PLATE 29—WOODY DICOTYLEDONOUS STEM : TILIA

T.S. Tilia stem 4th year

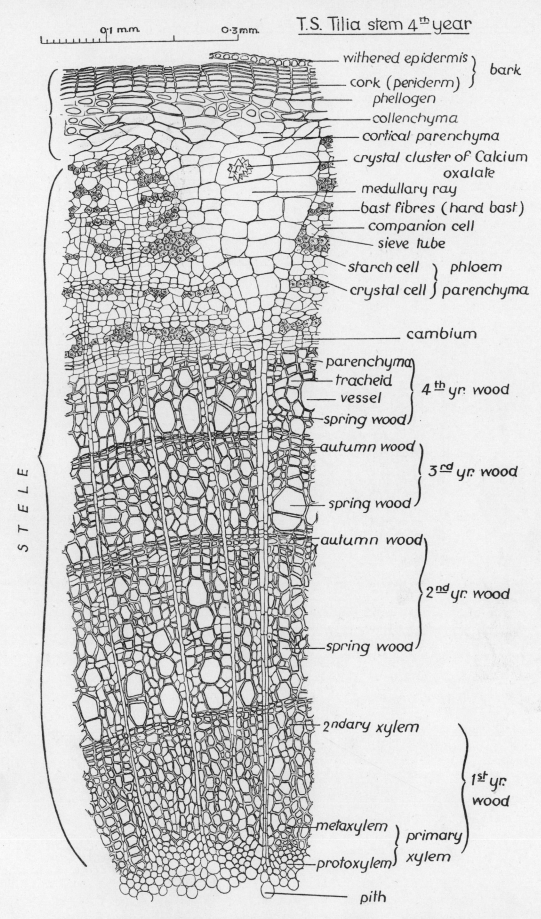

0·1 m.m.   0·3mm.

withered epidermis ⎫
cork (periderm) ⎬ bark
phellogen
collenchyma
cortical parenchyma
crystal cluster of Calcium oxalate
medullary ray
bast fibres (hard bast)
companion cell
sieve tube
starch cell ⎫ phloem
crystal cell ⎬ parenchyma

cambium

parenchyma ⎫
tracheid
vessel ⎬ 4th yr. wood
spring wood ⎭

autumn wood ⎫
⎬ 3rd yr. wood
spring wood ⎭

autumn wood ⎫

⎬ 2nd yr. wood

spring wood ⎭

2ndary xylem

⎫ 1st yr. wood

metaxylem ⎫ primary
protoxylem ⎬ xylem

pith

STELE

PLATE 30—WOODY DICOTYLEDONOUS STEM : TILIA—Continued

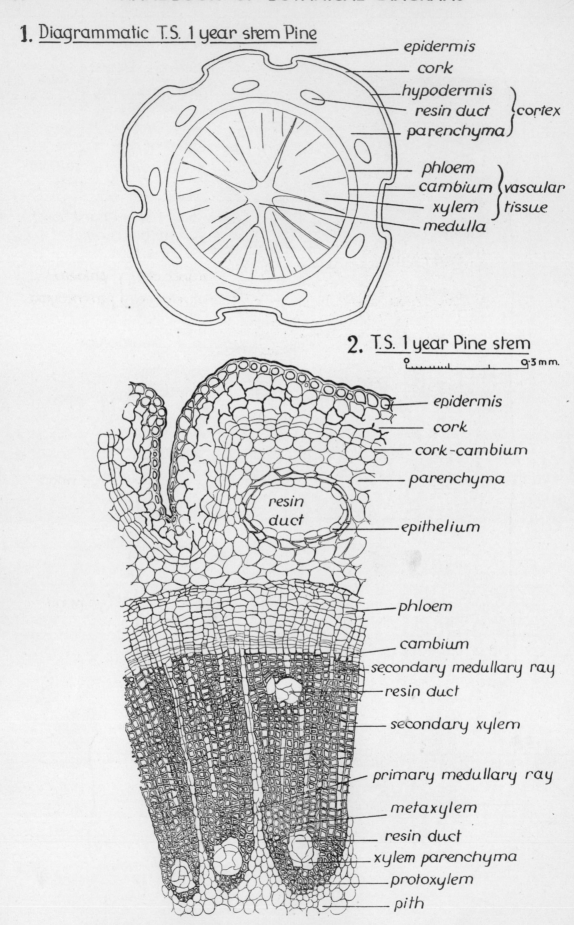

1. <u>Diagrammatic T.S. 1 year stem Pine</u>

- epidermis
- cork
- hypodermis
- resin duct   } cortex
- parenchyma
- phloem
- cambium   } vascular tissue
- xylem
- medulla

2. <u>T.S. 1 year Pine stem</u>

0   0·3 mm.

- epidermis
- cork
- cork-cambium
- parenchyma
- resin duct
- epithelium
- phloem
- cambium
- secondary medullary ray
- resin duct
- secondary xylem
- primary medullary ray
- metaxylem
- resin duct
- xylem parenchyma
- protoxylem
- pith

PLATE 31—WOODY GYMNOSPERMOUS STEM : PINUS

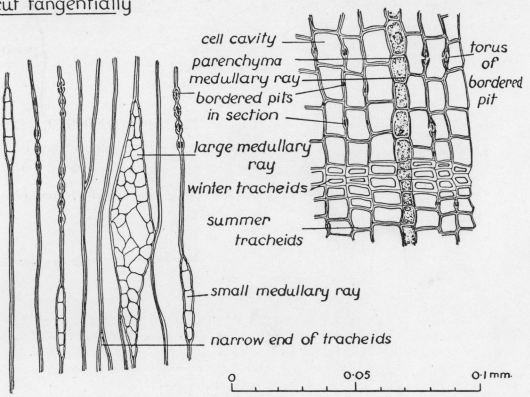

1. Transverse section
Wood of Pinus

2. Longitudinal section;
cut tangentially

cell cavity
parenchyma
medullary ray
bordered pits
in section
large medullary
ray
winter tracheids
summer
tracheids

torus
of
bordered
pit

small medullary ray

narrow end of tracheids

0   0·05   0·1 mm.

3. Longitudinal section, cut radially

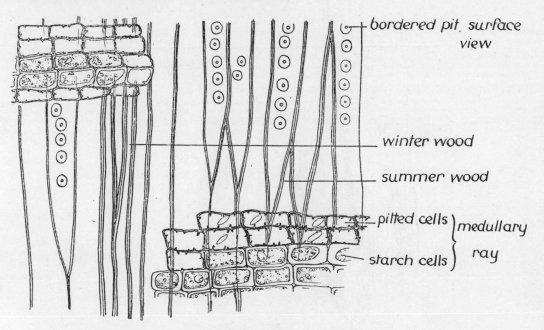

bordered pit surface
view

winter wood

summer wood

pitted cells } medullary

starch cells } ray

PLATE 32—WOODY GYMNOSPERMOUS STEM : PINUS—*Continued*

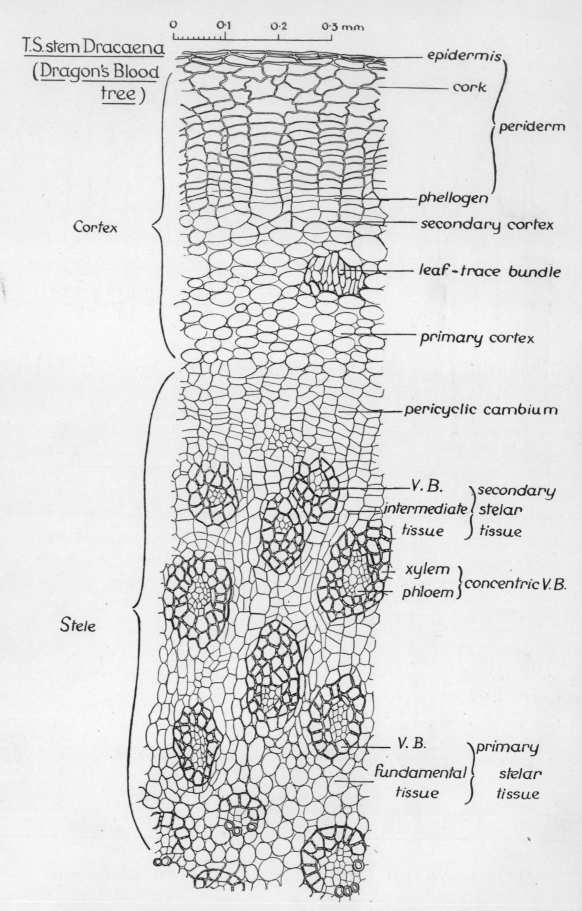

T.S.stem Dracaena
(Dragon's Blood
tree)

0   0·1   0·2   0·3 mm

epidermis

cork

periderm

Cortex

phellogen

secondary cortex

leaf-trace bundle

primary cortex

pericyclic cambium

V. B.
intermediate
tissue
} secondary
stelar
tissue

xylem
phloem
} concentric V.B.

Stele

V. B.
fundamental
tissue
} primary
stelar
tissue

PLATE 33—MONOCOTYLEDONOUS STEM : SECONDARY GROWTH

T.S. stem Hippuris (Mare's Tail)

0 _ _ _ _ _ _ 0.4 mm.

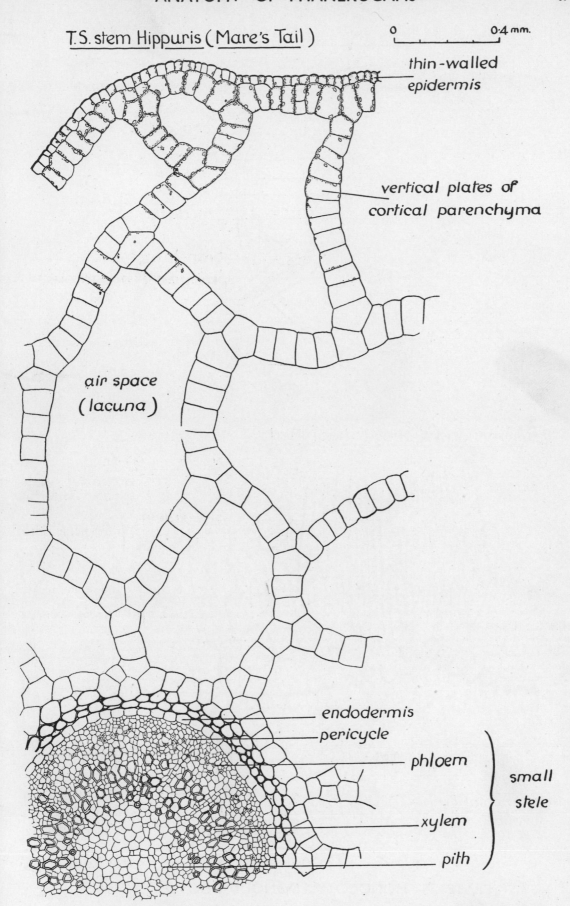

thin-walled
epidermis

vertical plates of
cortical parenchyma

air space
(lacuna)

endodermis
pericycle
phloem

small
stele

xylem

pith

PLATE 34—DICOTYLEDONOUS HYDROPHYTE STEM : HIPPURIS

1. T.S. aerial "buttress" root of Maize

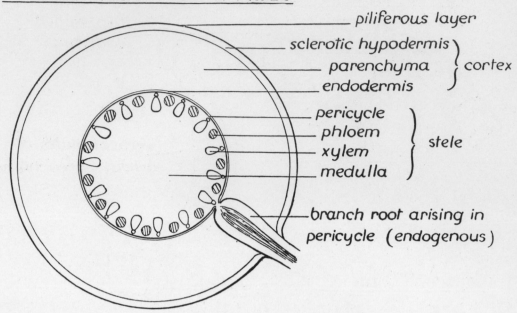

piliferous layer
sclerotic hypodermis
parenchyma ⎱ cortex
endodermis

pericycle
phloem ⎱ stele
xylem
medulla

branch root arising in pericycle (endogenous)

2. A portion of above, magnified

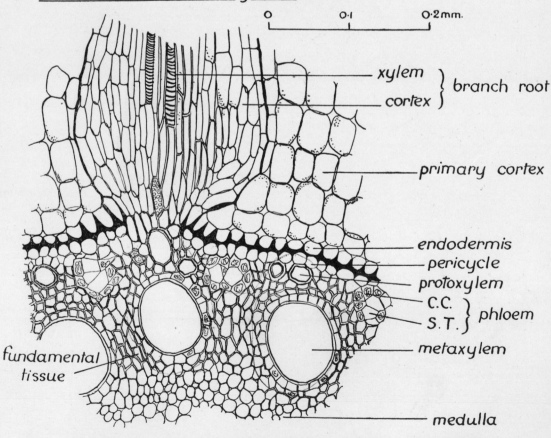

0   0.1   0.2mm.

xylem ⎱ branch root
cortex

primary cortex

endodermis
pericycle
protoxylem
C.C. ⎱ phloem
S.T.
metaxylem

fundamental tissue

medulla

PLATE 35—MONOCOTYLEDONOUS ROOT : ZEA MAIS

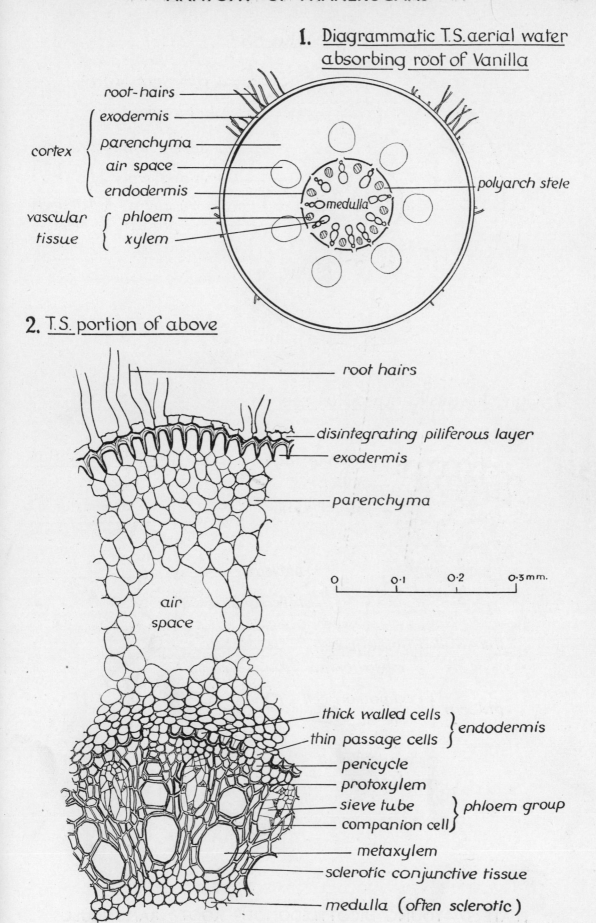

1. Diagrammatic T.S. aerial water absorbing root of Vanilla

root-hairs

cortex {
exodermis
parenchyma
air space
endodermis
}

vascular tissue {
phloem
xylem
}

medulla

polyarch stele

2. T.S. portion of above

root hairs

disintegrating piliferous layer

exodermis

parenchyma

0   0·1   0·2   0·3 mm.

air space

thick walled cells } endodermis
thin passage cells }

pericycle

protoxylem

sieve tube } phloem group
companion cell }

metaxylem

sclerotic conjunctive tissue

medulla (often sclerotic)

PLATE 36—MONOCOTYLEDONOUS ROOT : VANILLA

1. <u>Diagrammatic T.S. Ranunculus root</u>

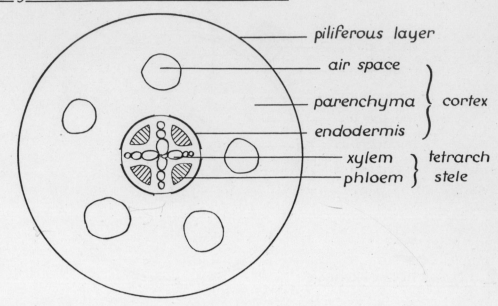

- piliferous layer
- air space
- parenchyma ⎫
- endodermis ⎬ cortex
- xylem ⎫ tetrarch
- phloem ⎬ stele

2. <u>Outer tissues Ranunculus root</u>

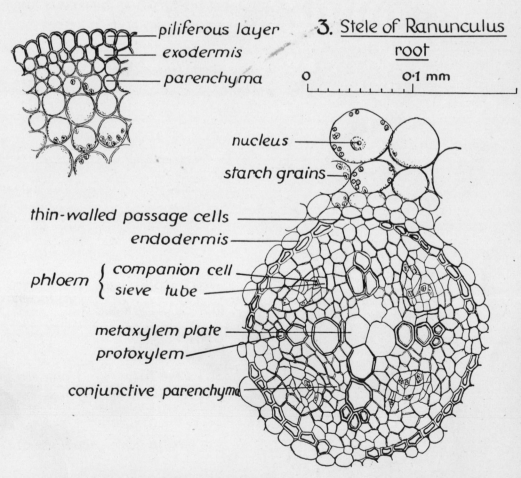

- piliferous layer
- exodermis
- parenchyma

3. <u>Stele of Ranunculus root</u>

0   0·1 mm

- nucleus
- starch grains
- thin-walled passage cells
- endodermis
- phloem { companion cell
-          sieve tube
- metaxylem plate
- protoxylem
- conjunctive parenchyma

PLATE 37—YOUNG DICOTYLEDONOUS ROOT : RANUNCULUS

Pentarch root of Vicia Faba

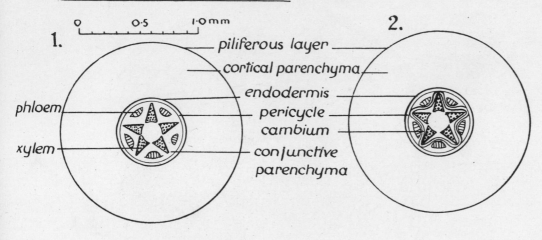

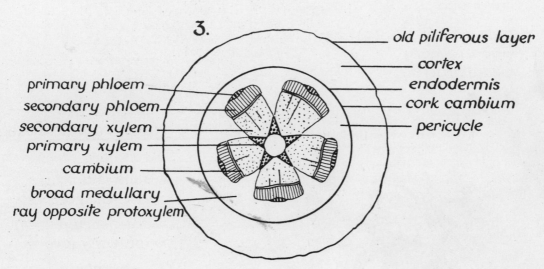

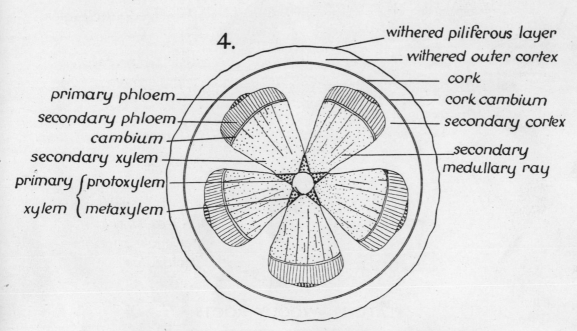

PLATE 38—ROOTS : SECONDARY GROWTH

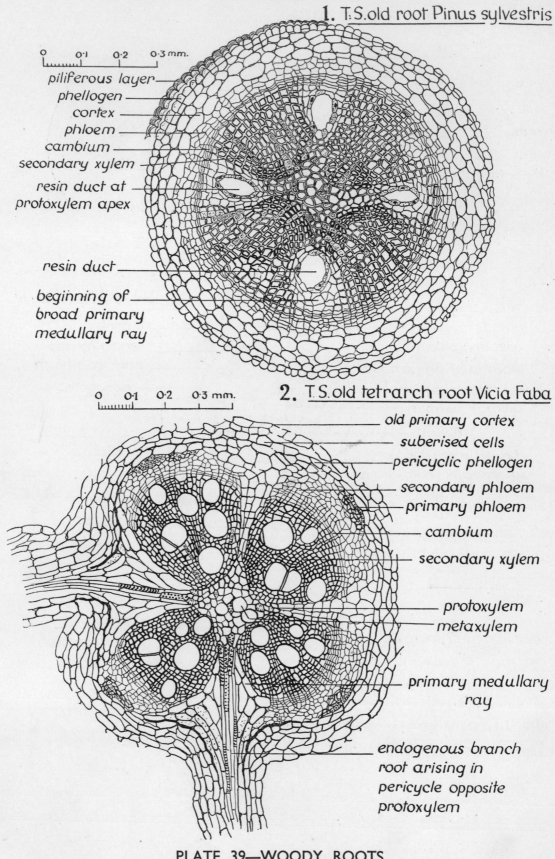

1. T.S.old root Pinus sylvestris

0   0·1   0·2   0·3 mm.

piliferous layer
phellogen
cortex
phloem
cambium
secondary xylem
resin duct at
protoxylem apex

resin duct

beginning of
broad primary
medullary ray

0   0·1   0·2   0·3 mm.

2. T.S.old tetrarch root Vicia Faba

old primary cortex
suberised cells
pericyclic phellogen
secondary phloem
primary phloem
cambium
secondary xylem

protoxylem
metaxylem

primary medullary
ray

endogenous branch
root arising in
pericycle opposite
protoxylem

PLATE 39—WOODY ROOTS

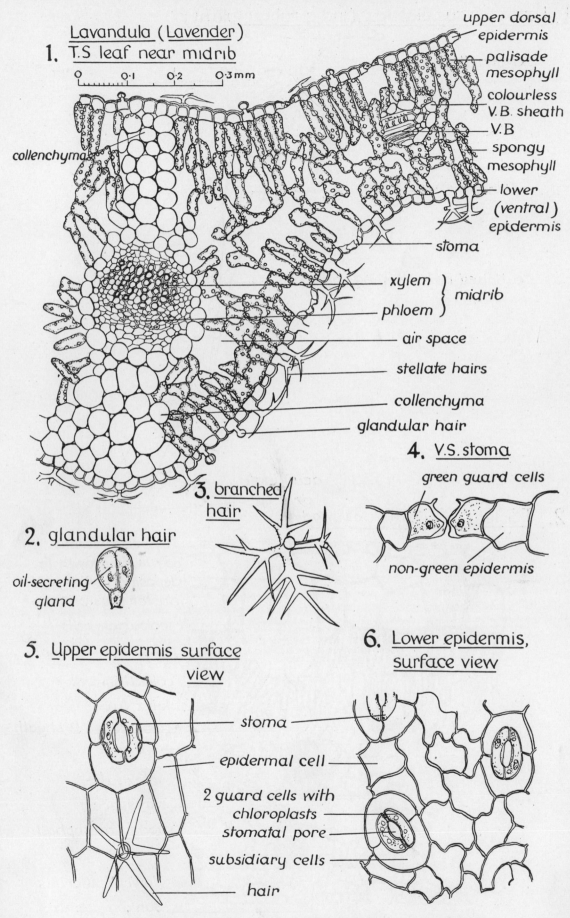

Lavandula (Lavender)
1. T.S leaf near midrib

0   0·1   0·2   0·3 mm

upper dorsal epidermis
palisade mesophyll
colourless V.B. sheath
V.B
spongy mesophyll
lower (ventral) epidermis
stoma
collenchyma
xylem ⎫
phloem ⎭ midrib
air space
stellate hairs
collenchyma
glandular hair

2. glandular hair

oil-secreting gland

3. branched hair

4. V.S. stoma

green guard cells

non-green epidermis

5. Upper epidermis surface view

6. Lower epidermis, surface view

stoma
epidermal cell
2 guard cells with chloroplasts
stomatal pore
subsidiary cells
hair

PLATE 40—DICOTYLEDONOUS LEAF : LAVANDULA

1. <u>Leaf of Ficus elastica</u> (India rubber plant)

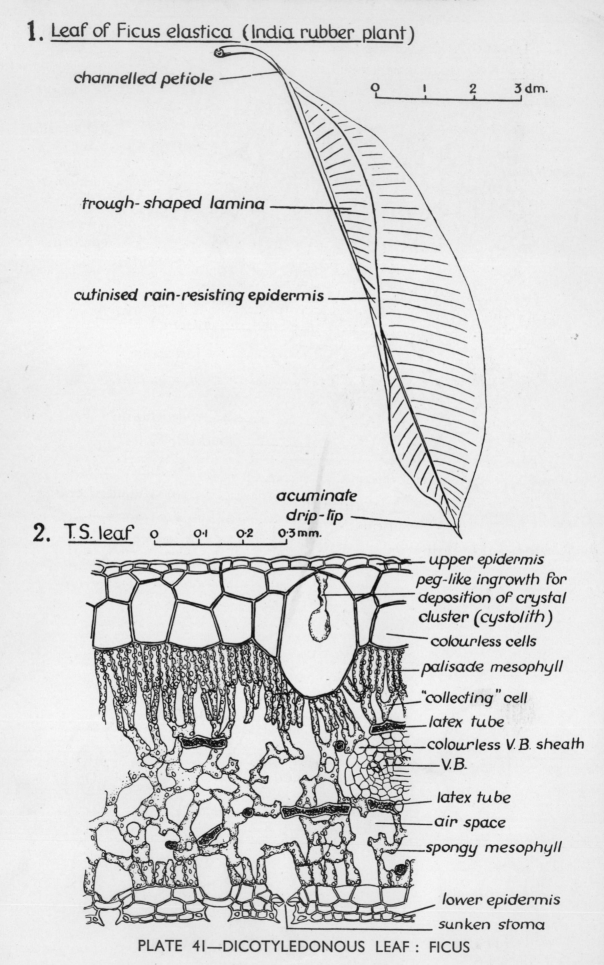

channelled petiole

0　　1　　2　　3 dm.

trough-shaped lamina

cutinised rain-resisting epidermis

acuminate
drip-tip

2. <u>T.S. leaf</u>　0　　0·1　　0·2　　0·3 mm.

upper epidermis
peg-like ingrowth for
deposition of crystal
cluster (cystolith)
colourless cells
palisade mesophyll
"collecting" cell
latex tube
colourless V.B. sheath
V.B.
latex tube
air space
spongy mesophyll
lower epidermis
sunken stoma

PLATE 41—DICOTYLEDONOUS LEAF : FICUS

1. Diagrammatic T.S. Iris leaf

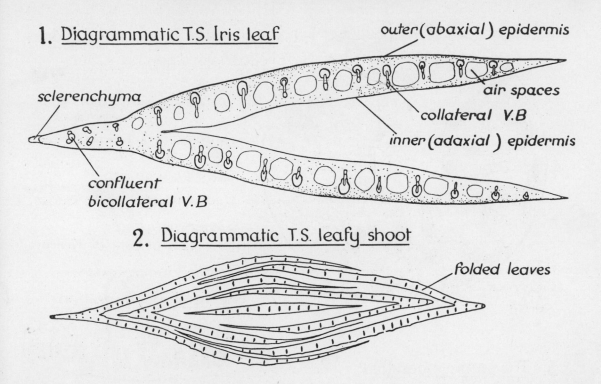

outer (abaxial) epidermis

sclerenchyma

air spaces

collateral V.B

inner (adaxial) epidermis

confluent bicollateral V.B

2. Diagrammatic T.S. leafy shoot

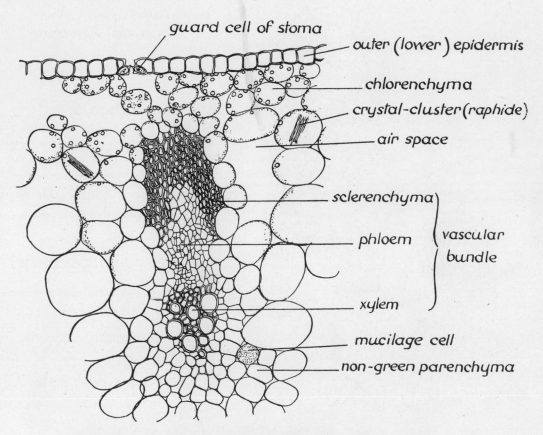

folded leaves

3. V.S. leaf through V.B.

guard cell of stoma

outer (lower) epidermis

chlorenchyma

crystal-cluster (raphide)

air space

sclerenchyma

phloem

vascular bundle

xylem

mucilage cell

non-green parenchyma

PLATE 42—MONOCOTYLEDONOUS LEAF : IRIS

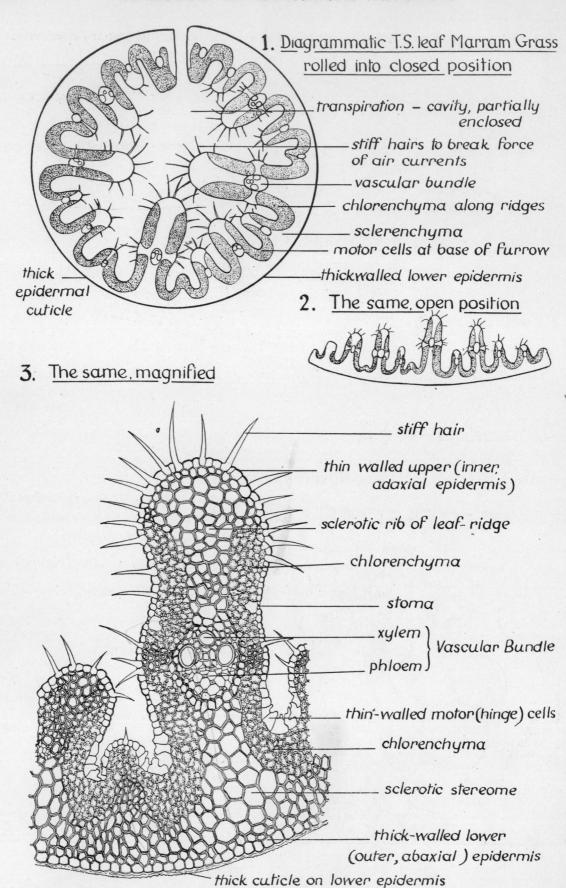

1. Diagrammatic T.S. leaf Marram Grass rolled into closed position

transpiration – cavity, partially enclosed

stiff hairs to break force of air currents

vascular bundle

chlorenchyma along ridges

sclerenchyma

motor cells at base of furrow

thickwalled lower epidermis

thick epidermal cuticle

2. The same, open position

3. The same, magnified

stiff hair

thin walled upper (inner, adaxial epidermis)

sclerotic rib of leaf-ridge

chlorenchyma

stoma

xylem
phloem } Vascular Bundle

thin-walled motor (hinge) cells

chlorenchyma

sclerotic stereome

thick-walled lower (outer, abaxial) epidermis

thick cuticle on lower epidermis

PLATE 43—XEROPHYTIC LEAF : PSAMMA

1. Diagrammatic T.S. leaf (<u>centric type</u>) Pinus sylvestris

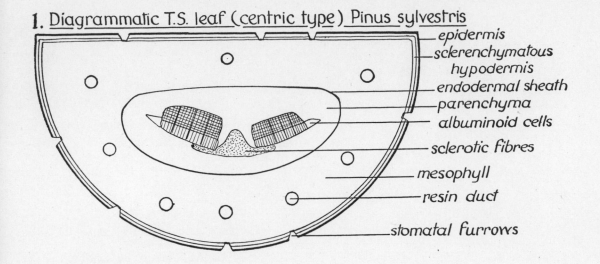

— epidermis
— sclerenchymatous hypodermis
— endodermal sheath
— parenchyma
— albuminoid cells
— sclerotic fibres
— mesophyll
— resin duct
— stomatal furrows

2. T.S. portion of leaf

0   0·1   0·2   0·3 mm.

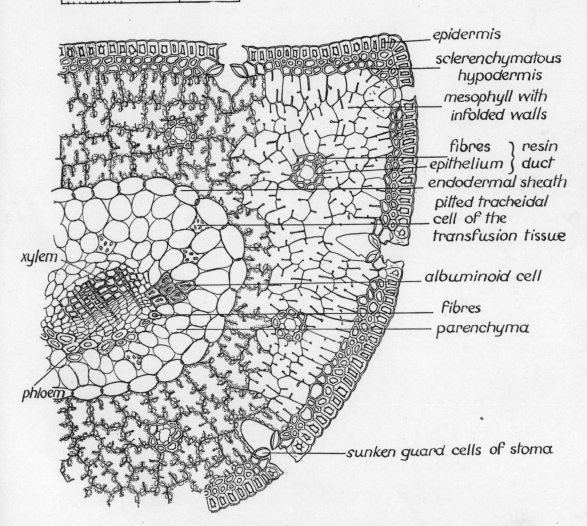

— epidermis
— sclerenchymatous hypodermis
— mesophyll with infolded walls
— fibres } resin
— epithelium } duct
— endodermal sheath
— pitted tracheidal cell of the transfusion tissue
— albuminoid cell
— fibres
— parenchyma
— sunken guard cells of stoma

xylem

phloem

PLATE 44—GYMNOSPERMOUS LEAF : PINUS

TAXONOMY OF CRYPTOGAMS

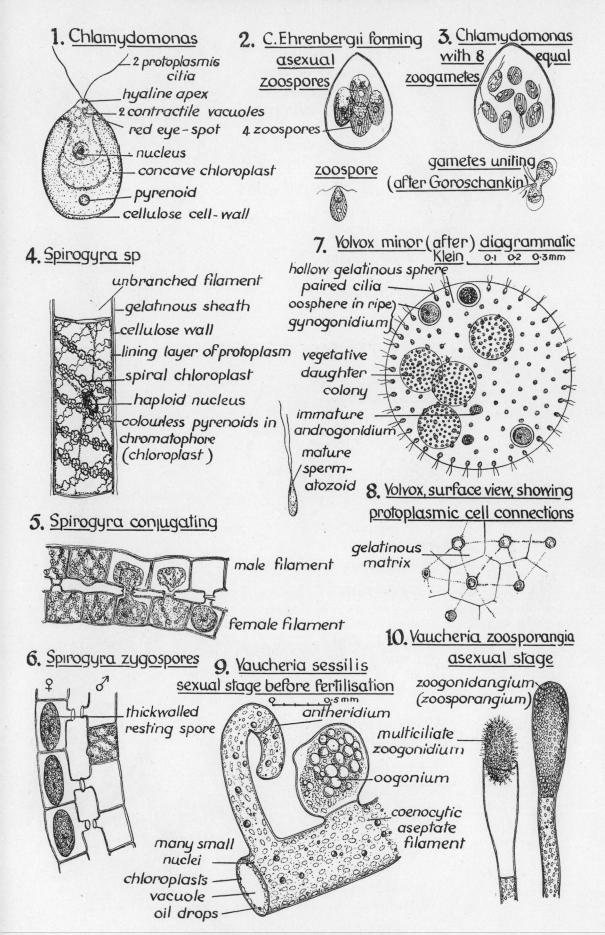

1. Chlamydomonas
- 2 protoplasmic cilia
- hyaline apex
- 2 contractile vacuoles
- red eye-spot
- nucleus
- concave chloroplast
- pyrenoid
- cellulose cell-wall

2. C.Ehrenbergii forming asexual zoospores
- 4 zoospores
- zoospore

3. Chlamydomonas with 8 equal zoogametes
- gametes uniting (after Goroschankin)

4. Spirogyra sp
- unbranched filament
- gelatinous sheath
- cellulose wall
- lining layer of protoplasm
- spiral chloroplast
- haploid nucleus
- colourless pyrenoids in chromatophore (chloroplast)

7. Volvox minor (after) diagrammatic Klein 0·1 0·2 0·3mm
- hollow gelatinous sphere
- paired cilia
- oosphere in ripe gynogonidium
- vegetative daughter colony
- immature androgonidium
- mature spermatozoid

5. Spirogyra conjugating
- male filament
- female filament

8. Volvox, surface view, showing protoplasmic cell connections
- gelatinous matrix

6. Spirogyra zygospores
- ♀ ♂
- thickwalled resting spore

9. Vaucheria sessilis sexual stage before fertilisation 0 0·5mm
- antheridium
- multiciliate zoogonidium
- oogonium
- coenocytic aseptate filament
- many small nuclei
- chloroplasts
- vacuole
- oil drops

10. Vaucheria zoosporangia asexual stage
- zoogonidangium (zoosporangium)

PLATE 45—CHLOROPHYCEÆ

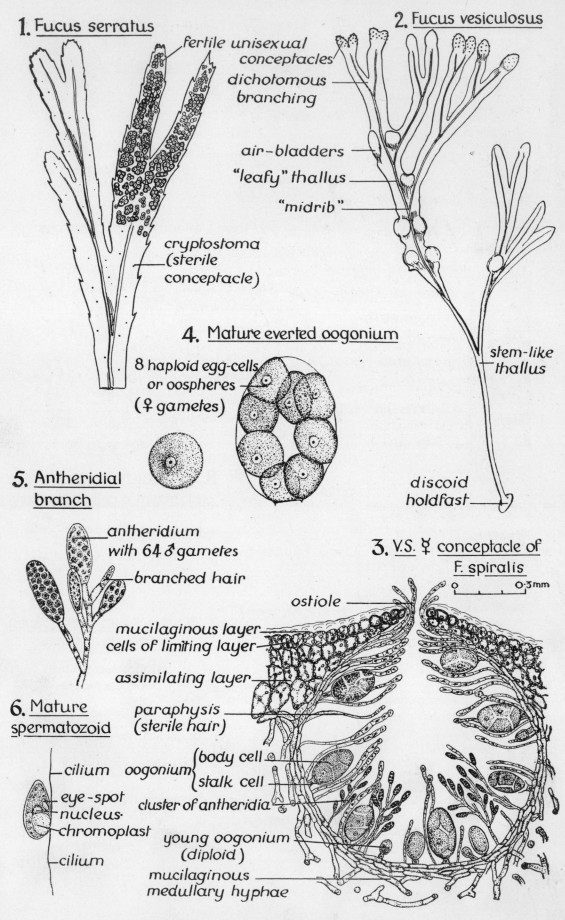

1. Fucus serratus

fertile unisexual conceptacles

dichotomous branching

cryptostoma (sterile conceptacle)

2. Fucus vesiculosus

air-bladders

"leafy" thallus

"midrib"

stem-like thallus

discoid holdfast

4. Mature everted oogonium

8 haploid egg-cells or oospheres (♀ gametes)

5. Antheridial branch

antheridium with 64 ♂ gametes

branched hair

3. V.S. ♀ conceptacle of F. spiralis

0   0·3mm

ostiole

mucilaginous layer
cells of limiting layer

assimilating layer

paraphysis (sterile hair)

6. Mature spermatozoid

cilium   oogonium { body cell
                         { stalk cell

eye-spot
nucleus
chromoplast

cluster of antheridia

young oogonium (diploid)

cilium

mucilaginous medullary hyphae

PLATE 46—PHÆOPHYCEÆ : FUCUS

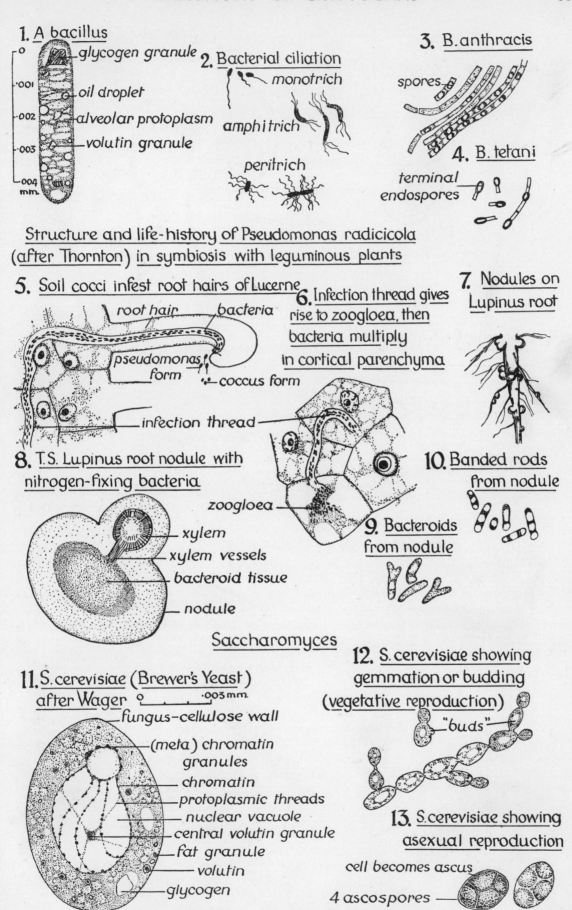

1. A bacillus
- glycogen granule
- oil droplet
- alveolar protoplasm
- volutin granule

2. Bacterial ciliation
- monotrich
- amphitrich
- peritrich

3. B. anthracis
- spores

4. B. tetani
- terminal endospores

Structure and life-history of Pseudomonas radicicola (after Thornton) in symbiosis with leguminous plants

5. Soil cocci infest root hairs of Lucerne
- root hair
- bacteria
- pseudomonas form
- coccus form
- infection thread

6. Infection thread gives rise to zoogloea, then bacteria multiply in cortical parenchyma

7. Nodules on Lupinus root

8. T.S. Lupinus root nodule with nitrogen-fixing bacteria
- zoogloea
- xylem
- xylem vessels
- bacteroid tissue
- nodule

9. Bacteroids from nodule

10. Banded rods from nodule

Saccharomyces

11. S. cerevisiae (Brewer's Yeast) after Wager   0 ___.___ ·003 mm.
- fungus-cellulose wall
- (meta) chromatin granules
- chromatin
- protoplasmic threads
- nuclear vacuole
- central volutin granule
- fat granule
- volutin
- glycogen

12. S. cerevisiae showing gemmation or budding (vegetative reproduction)
- "buds"

13. S. cerevisiae showing asexual reproduction
- cell becomes ascus
- 4 ascospores

PLATE 47—FUNGI : BACTERIA AND SACCHAROMYCES

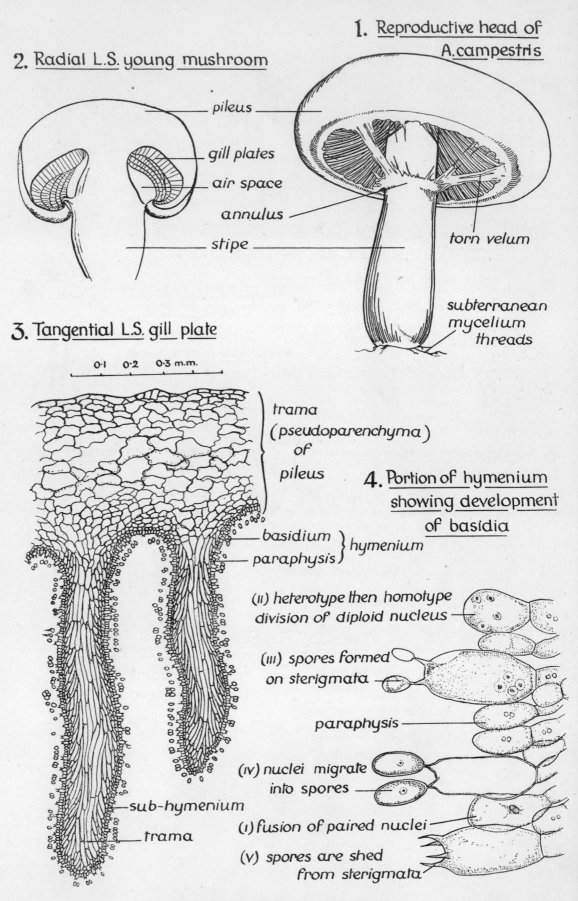

1. Reproductive head of _A. campestris_

2. Radial L.S. young mushroom

pileus

gill plates

air space

annulus

stipe

torn velum

subterranean mycelium threads

3. Tangential L.S. gill plate

0·1   0·2   0·3 m.m.

trama (pseudoparenchyma) of pileus

4. Portion of hymenium showing development of basidia

basidium } hymenium
paraphysis }

(II) heterotype then homotype division of diploid nucleus

(III) spores formed on sterigmata

paraphysis

(IV) nuclei migrate into spores

sub-hymenium

(I) fusion of paired nuclei

trama

(V) spores are shed from sterigmata

PLATE 48—FUNGI : AGARICUS

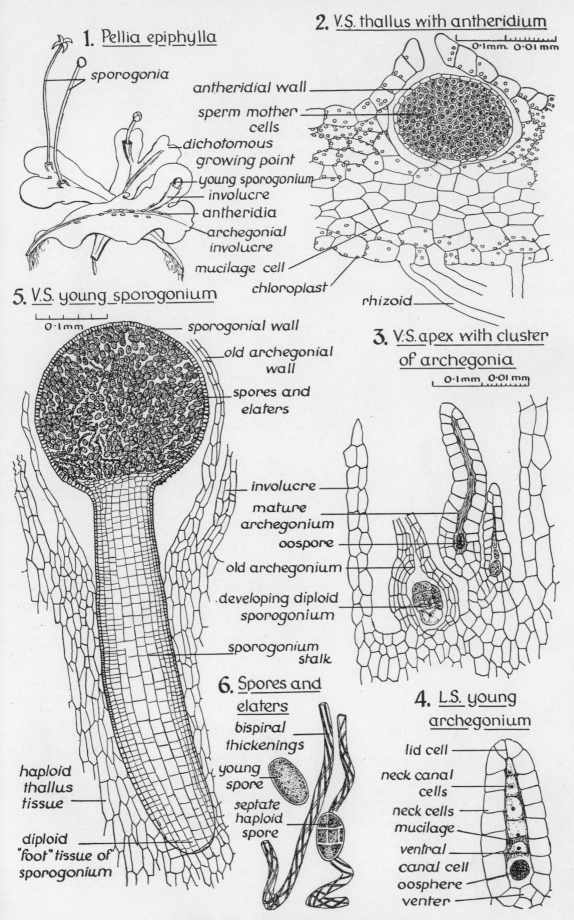

1. Pellia epiphylla
   - sporogonia

2. V.S. thallus with antheridium
   - 0·1mm. 0·01 mm
   - antheridial wall
   - sperm mother cells
   - dichotomous growing point
   - young sporogonium
   - involucre
   - antheridia
   - archegonial involucre
   - mucilage cell
   - chloroplast
   - rhizoid

5. V.S. young sporogonium
   - 0·1mm
   - sporogonial wall
   - old archegonial wall
   - spores and elaters
   - involucre
   - sporogonium stalk
   - haploid thallus tissue
   - diploid "foot" tissue of sporogonium

3. V.S. apex with cluster of archegonia
   - 0·1mm   0·01 mm
   - involucre
   - mature archegonium
   - oospore
   - old archegonium
   - developing diploid sporogonium

6. Spores and elaters
   - bispiral thickenings
   - young spore
   - septate haploid spore

4. L.S. young archegonium
   - lid cell
   - neck canal cells
   - neck cells
   - mucilage
   - ventral canal cell
   - oosphere
   - venter

PLATE 49—HEPATICÆ : PELLIA

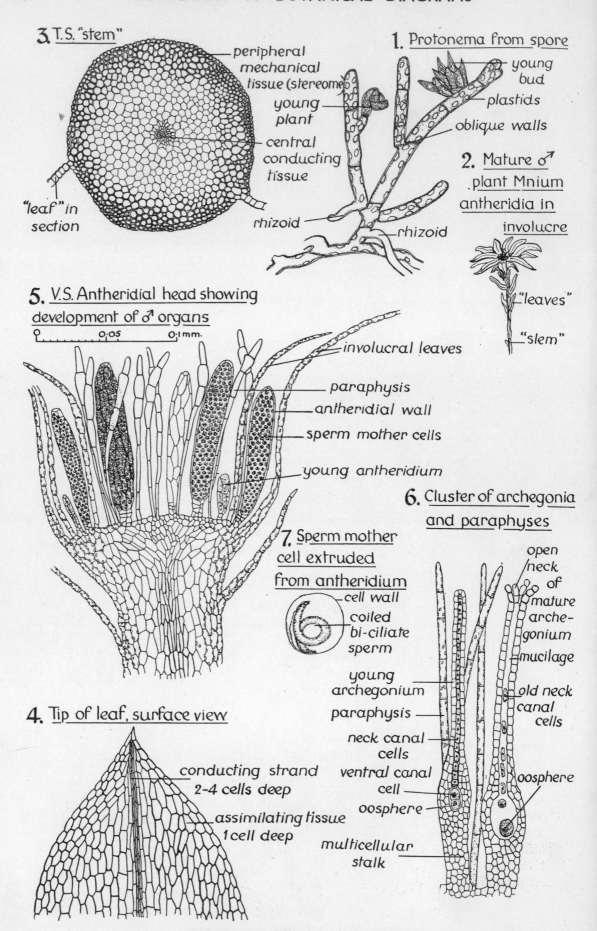

3. T.S. "stem"

peripheral mechanical tissue (stereome)

young plant

central conducting tissue

"leaf" in section

rhizoid

1. Protonema from spore

young bud

plastids

oblique walls

rhizoid

2. Mature ♂ plant Mnium antheridia in involucre

"leaves"

"stem"

5. V.S. Antheridial head showing development of ♂ organs

0   0.05   0.1 mm.

involucral leaves

paraphysis

antheridial wall

sperm mother cells

young antheridium

6. Cluster of archegonia and paraphyses

open neck of mature arche-gonium

mucilage

old neck canal cells

7. Sperm mother cell extruded from antheridium

cell wall

coiled bi-ciliate sperm

young archegonium

paraphysis

neck canal cells

ventral canal cell

oosphere

oosphere

multicellular stalk

4. Tip of leaf, surface view

conducting strand 2-4 cells deep

assimilating tissue 1 cell deep

PLATE 50—MUSCI : FUNARIA

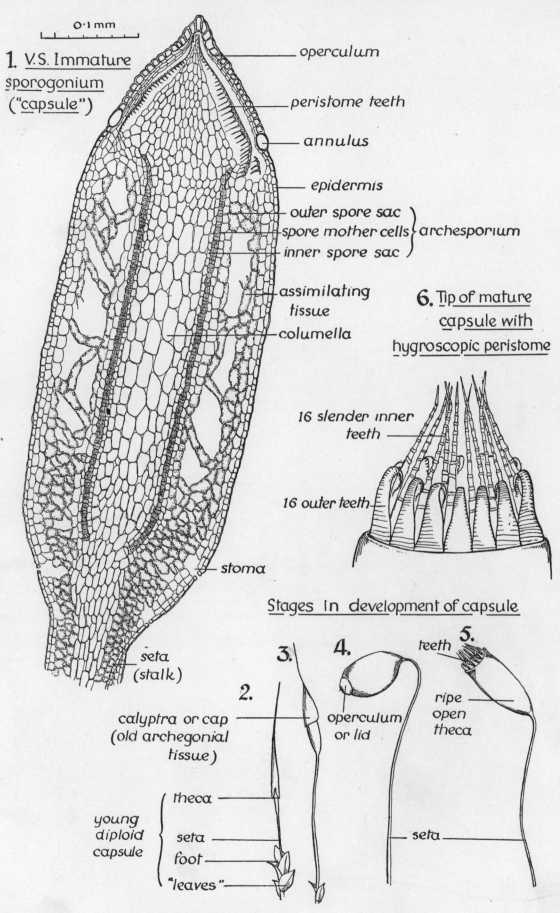

0·1 mm

1. V.S. Immature sporogonium ("capsule")

operculum

peristome teeth

annulus

epidermis

outer spore sac
spore mother cells } archesporium
inner spore sac

assimilating tissue

columella

6. Tip of mature capsule with hygroscopic peristome

16 slender inner teeth

16 outer teeth

stoma

seta (stalk)

Stages in development of capsule

3.

4.

teeth 5.

calyptra or cap (old archegonial tissue)

operculum or lid

ripe open theca

young diploid capsule {
theca

seta

foot

"leaves"

seta

PLATE 51—MUSCI : FUNARIA—*Continued*

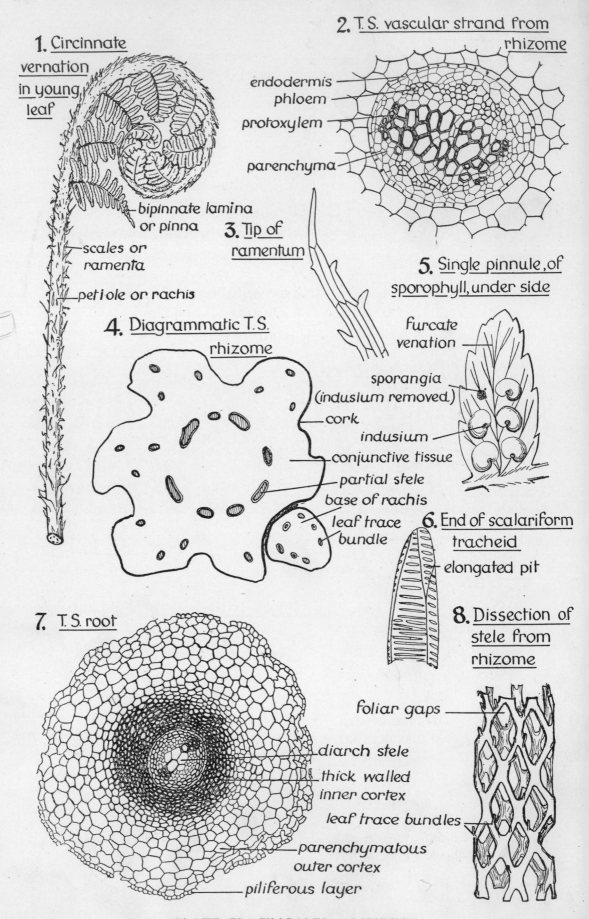

1. Circinnate vernation in young leaf

— bipinnate lamina or pinna

3. Tip of ramentum

— scales or ramenta

— petiole or rachis

2. T.S. vascular strand from rhizome

endodermis
phloem
protoxylem

parenchyma

4. Diagrammatic T.S. rhizome

cork
conjunctive tissue
partial stele
base of rachis
leaf trace bundle

5. Single pinnule, of sporophyll, under side

furcate venation

sporangia (indusium removed.)

indusium

6. End of scalariform tracheid
— elongated pit

7. T.S. root

diarch stele

thick walled inner cortex

leaf trace bundles

parenchymatous outer cortex

piliferous layer

8. Dissection of stele from rhizome

foliar gaps

PLATE 52—FILICALES : ASPIDIUM

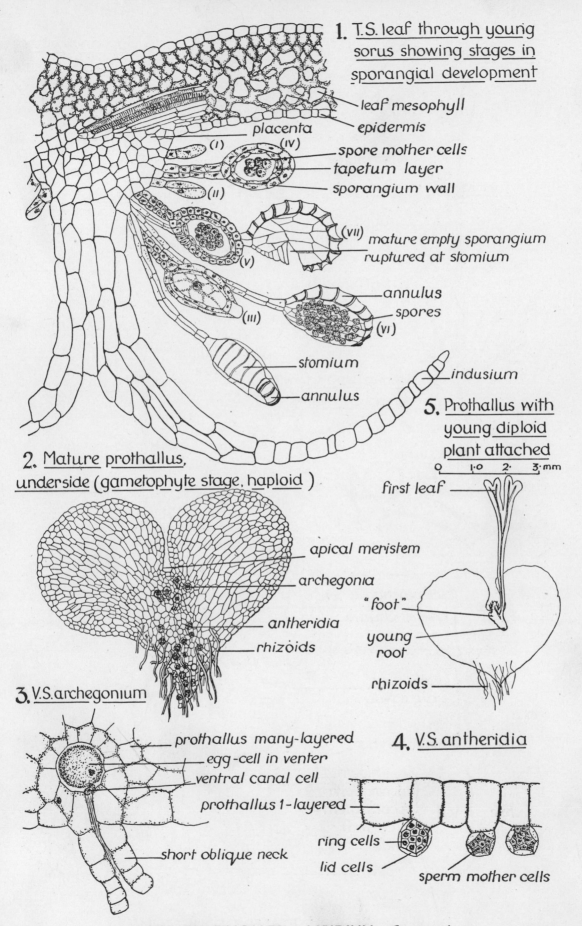

1. T.S. leaf through young sorus showing stages in sporangial development

- leaf mesophyll
- placenta
- epidermis
- (I)
- (IV)
- spore mother cells
- tapetum layer
- sporangium wall
- (II)
- (VII) mature empty sporangium ruptured at stomium
- (V)
- annulus
- spores
- (III)
- (VI)
- stomium
- annulus
- indusium

2. Mature prothallus, underside (gametophyte stage, haploid)

- apical meristem
- archegonia
- antheridia
- rhizoids

5. Prothallus with young diploid plant attached

0 1·0 2· 3· mm

- first leaf
- "foot"
- young root
- rhizoids

3. V.S. archegonium

- prothallus many-layered
- egg-cell in venter
- ventral canal cell
- prothallus 1-layered
- short oblique neck

4. V.S. antheridia

- ring cells
- lid cells
- sperm mother cells

PLATE 53—FILICALES : ASPIDIUM—*Continued*

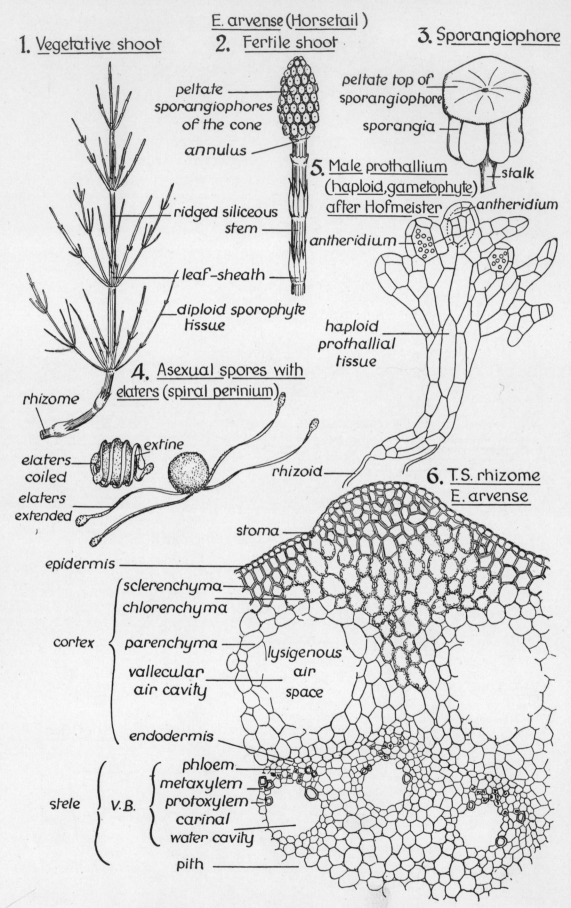

E. arvense (Horsetail)

1. Vegetative shoot
2. Fertile shoot
3. Sporangiophore

peltate sporangiophores of the cone
annulus
peltate top of sporangiophore
sporangia
stalk

5. Male prothallium (haploid, gametophyte) after Hofmeister

ridged siliceous stem
antheridium
antheridium

leaf-sheath

diploid sporophyte tissue

haploid prothallial tissue

rhizome

4. Asexual spores with elaters (spiral perinium)

extine
elaters coiled
elaters extended
rhizoid

6. T.S. rhizome E. arvense

stoma

epidermis

cortex {
sclerenchyma
chlorenchyma
parenchyma
vallecular air cavity
endodermis
}

lysigenous air space

stele { V.B. {
phloem
metaxylem
protoxylem
carinal
water cavity
}
pith

PLATE 54—EQUISETALES : EQUISETUM

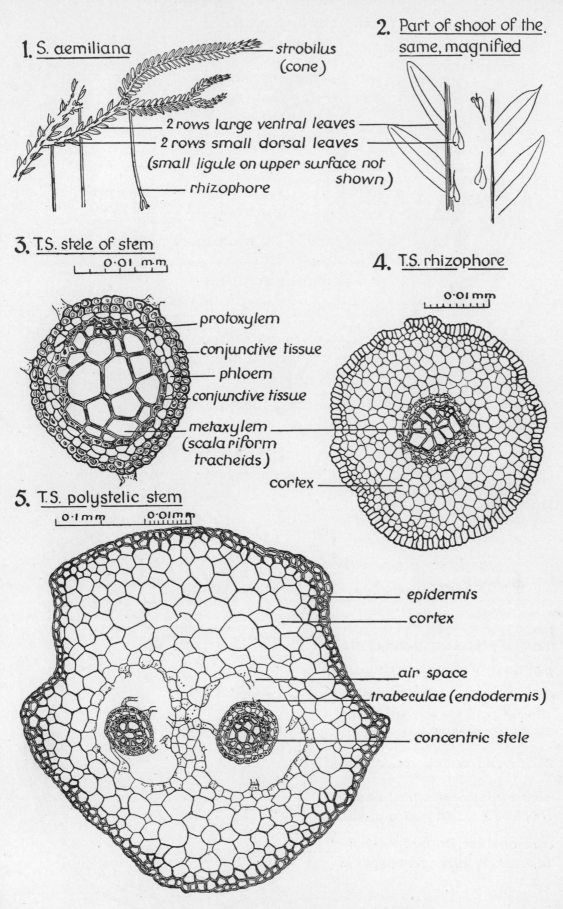

1. S. aemiliana — strobilus (cone)

2. Part of shoot of the same, magnified

2 rows large ventral leaves
2 rows small dorsal leaves
(small ligule on upper surface not shown)
rhizophore

3. T.S. stele of stem
0·01 m.m

protoxylem
conjunctive tissue
phloem
conjunctive tissue
metaxylem (scalariform tracheids)

4. T.S. rhizophore
0·01 mm

cortex

5. T.S. polystelic stem
0·1 mm   0·01 mm

epidermis
cortex

air space
trabeculae (endodermis)

concentric stele

PLATE 55—LYCOPODIALES : SELAGINELLA

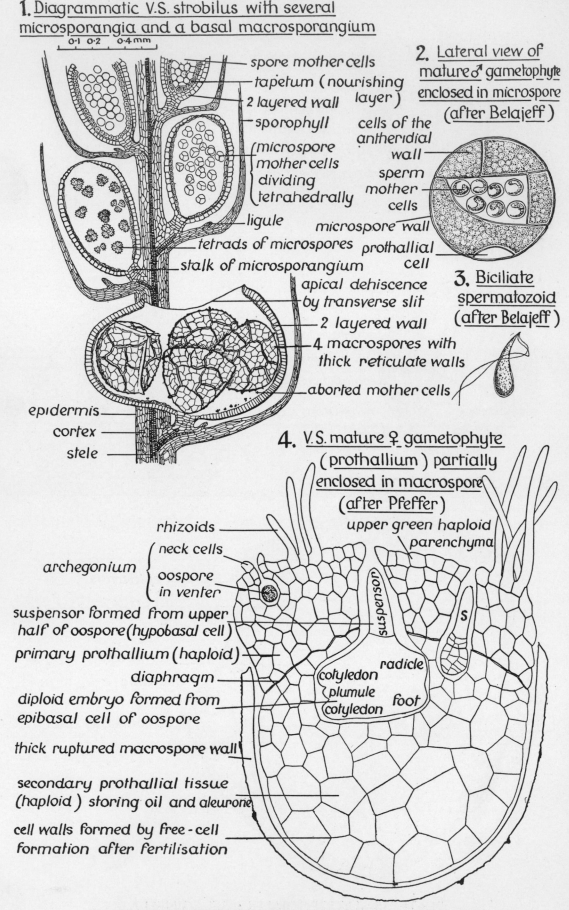

1. Diagrammatic V.S. strobilus with several microsporangia and a basal macrosporangium

0·1 0·2 0·4 mm

spore mother cells
tapetum (nourishing layer)
2 layered wall
sporophyll
microspore mother cells dividing tetrahedrally
ligule
tetrads of microspores
stalk of microsporangium
apical dehiscence by transverse slit
2 layered wall
4 macrospores with thick reticulate walls
aborted mother cells

epidermis
cortex
stele

2. Lateral view of mature ♂ gametophyte enclosed in microspore (after Belajeff)

cells of the antheridial wall
sperm mother cells
microspore wall
prothallial cell

3. Biciliate spermatozoid (after Belajeff)

4. V.S. mature ♀ gametophyte (prothallium) partially enclosed in macrospore (after Pfeffer)

rhizoids
archegonium { neck cells
oospore in venter
suspensor formed from upper half of oospore (hypobasal cell)
primary prothallium (haploid)
diaphragm
diploid embryo formed from epibasal cell of oospore
thick ruptured macrospore wall
secondary prothallial tissue (haploid) storing oil and aleurone
cell walls formed by free-cell formation after fertilisation

upper green haploid parenchyma
suspensor
radicle
cotyledon
plumule
cotyledon
foot
S

PLATE 56—LYCOPODIALES : SELAGINELLA—Continued

TAXONOMY OF PHANEROGAMS

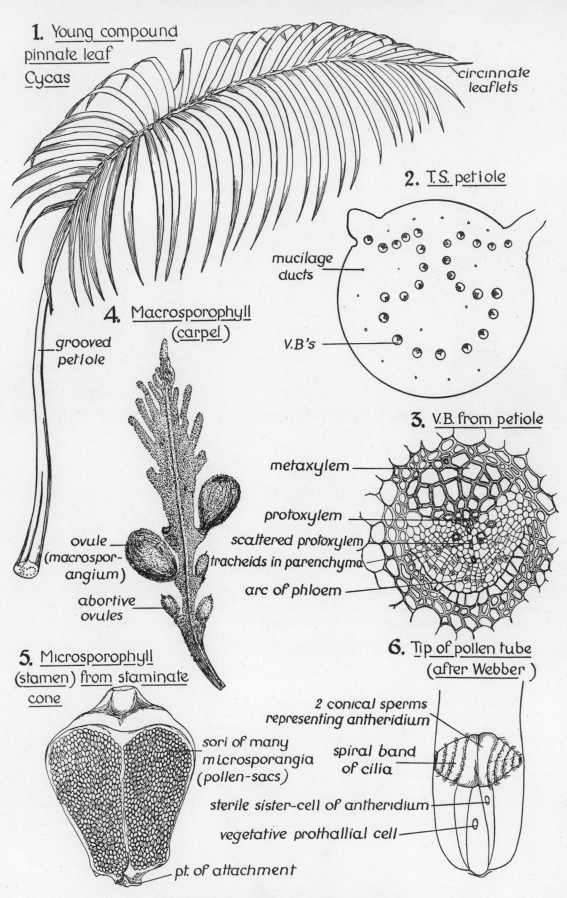

1. Young compound pinnate leaf Cycas

circinnate leaflets

2. T.S. petiole

mucilage ducts

V.B's

4. Macrosporophyll (carpel)

grooved petiole

ovule (macrosporangium)

abortive ovules

3. V.B. from petiole

metaxylem

protoxylem

scattered protoxylem

tracheids in parenchyma

arc of phloem

5. Microsporophyll (stamen) from staminate cone

sori of many microsporangia (pollen-sacs)

pt. of attachment

6. Tip of pollen tube (after Webber)

2 conical sperms representing antheridium

spiral band of cilia

sterile sister-cell of antheridium

vegetative prothallial cell

PLATE 57—CYCADALES : CYCAS

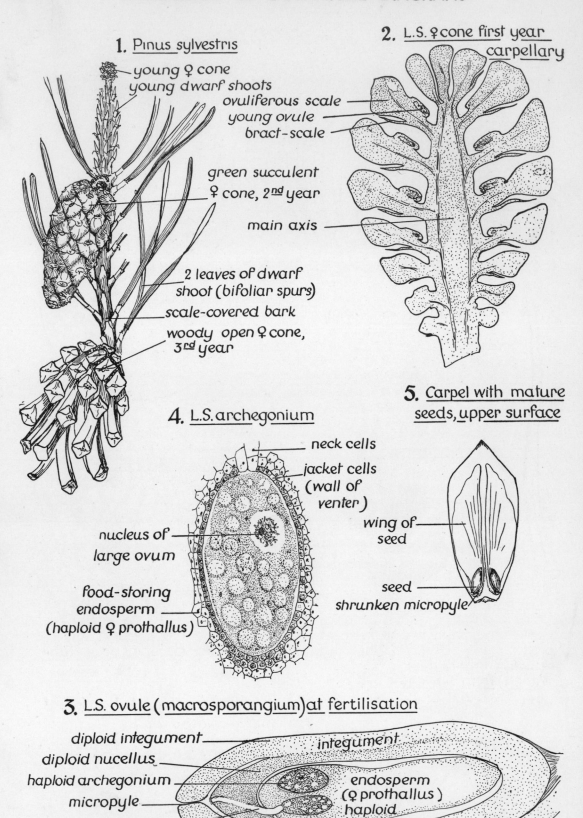

1. Pinus sylvestris
- young ♀ cone
- young dwarf shoots
- ovuliferous scale
- young ovule
- bract-scale
- green succulent ♀ cone, 2nd year
- main axis
- 2 leaves of dwarf shoot (bifoliar spurs)
- scale-covered bark
- woody open ♀ cone, 3rd year

2. L.S. ♀ cone first year carpellary

4. L.S. archegonium
- neck cells
- jacket cells (wall of venter)
- nucleus of large ovum
- food-storing endosperm (haploid ♀ prothallus)

5. Carpel with mature seeds, upper surface
- wing of seed
- seed
- shrunken micropyle

3. L.S. ovule (macrosporangium) at fertilisation
- diploid integument
- diploid nucellus
- haploid archegonium
- micropyle
- pollen tube
- embryo-sac (macrospore)
- integument
- endosperm (♀ prothallus) haploid
- integument
- ovuliferous scale

PLATE 58—CONIFERALES : PINUS

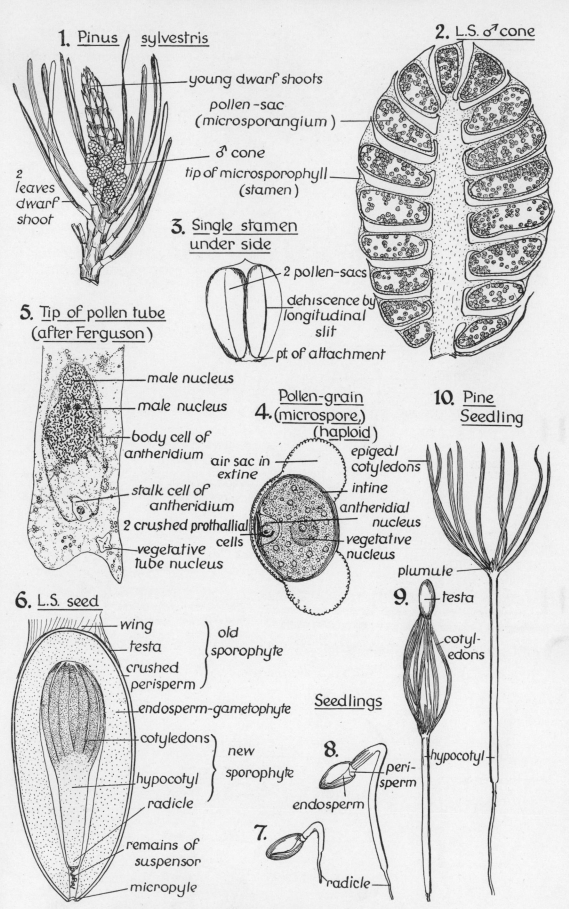

1. _Pinus_ _sylvestris_

young dwarf shoots

pollen-sac
(microsporangium)

♂ cone

tip of microsporophyll
(stamen)

2 leaves dwarf shoot

2. L.S. ♂ cone

3. Single stamen under side

2 pollen-sacs

dehiscence by longitudinal slit

pt. of attachment

5. Tip of pollen tube
(after Ferguson)

male nucleus

male nucleus

body cell of antheridium

stalk cell of antheridium

2 crushed prothallial cells

vegetative tube nucleus

Pollen-grain
4. (microspore,)
(haploid)

air sac in extine

epigeal cotyledons

intine

antheridial nucleus

vegetative nucleus

10. Pine Seedling

plumule

testa

cotyledons

hypocotyl

6. L.S. seed

wing

testa

crushed perisperm

old sporophyte

endosperm-gametophyte

cotyledons

hypocotyl

radicle

new sporophyte

remains of suspensor

micropyle

Seedlings

9.

8.

peri-sperm

endosperm

7.

radicle

PLATE 59—CONIFERALES : PINUS—_Continued_

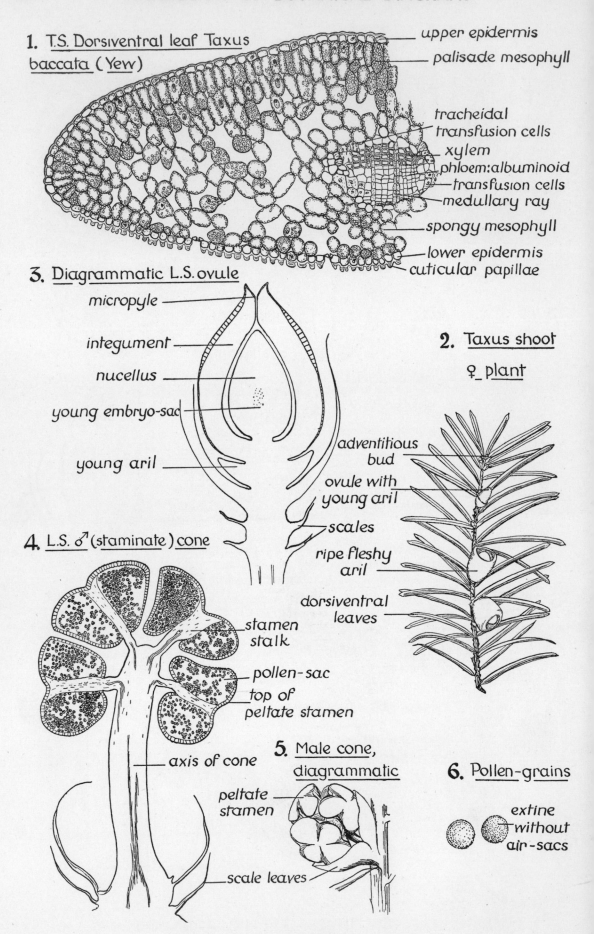

1. T.S. Dorsiventral leaf Taxus baccata (Yew)

upper epidermis
palisade mesophyll

tracheidal
transfusion cells
xylem
phloem: albuminoid
transfusion cells
medullary ray
spongy mesophyll
lower epidermis
cuticular papillae

3. Diagrammatic L.S. ovule

micropyle
integument
nucellus
young embryo-sac
young aril

2. Taxus shoot
♀ plant

adventitious bud
ovule with young aril
scales
ripe fleshy aril
dorsiventral leaves

4. L.S. ♂ (staminate) cone

stamen stalk
pollen-sac
top of peltate stamen
axis of cone

5. Male cone, diagrammatic

peltate stamen
scale leaves

6. Pollen-grains

extine without air-sacs

PLATE 60—CONIFERALES : TAXUS

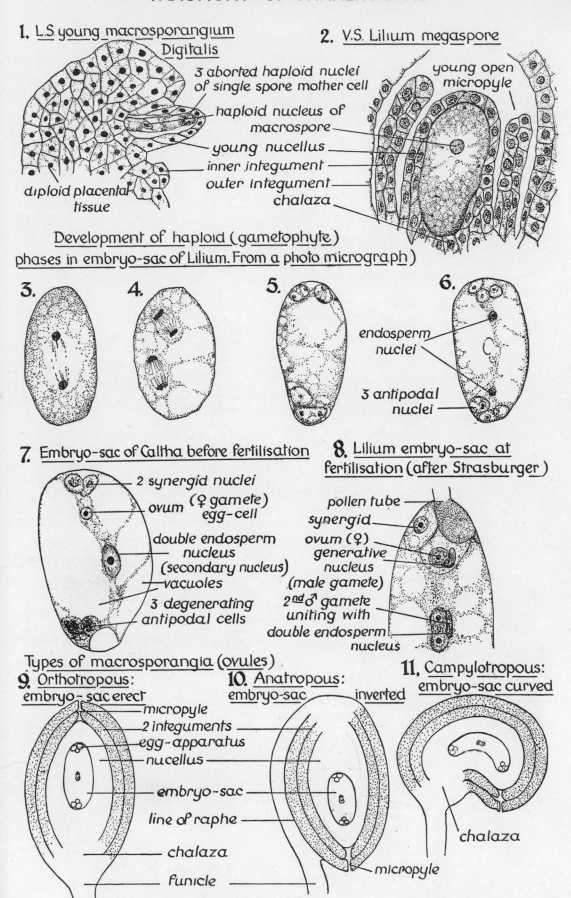

1. L.S young macrosporangium Digitalis

3 aborted haploid nuclei of single spore mother cell

haploid nucleus of macrospore

young nucellus

inner integument

outer integument

chalaza

diploid placental tissue

2. V.S. Lilium megaspore

young open micropyle

Development of haploid (gametophyte) phases in embryo-sac of Lilium. From a photo micrograph)

3.

4.

5.

6.

endosperm nuclei

3 antipodal nuclei

7. Embryo-sac of Caltha before fertilisation

2 synergid nuclei

ovum (♀ gamete) egg-cell

double endosperm nucleus (secondary nucleus)

vacuoles

3 degenerating antipodal cells

8. Lilium embryo-sac at fertilisation (after Strasburger)

pollen tube

synergid

ovum (♀)

generative nucleus (male gamete)

2nd ♂ gamete uniting with double endosperm nucleus

Types of macrosporangia (ovules)

9. Orthotropous: embryo-sac erect

micropyle

2 integuments

egg-apparatus

nucellus

embryo-sac

line of raphe

chalaza

funicle

10. Anatropous: embryo-sac inverted

micropyle

11. Campylotropous: embryo-sac curved

chalaza

micropyle

PLATE 61—ANGIOSPERMS : THE MACROSPORANGIUM

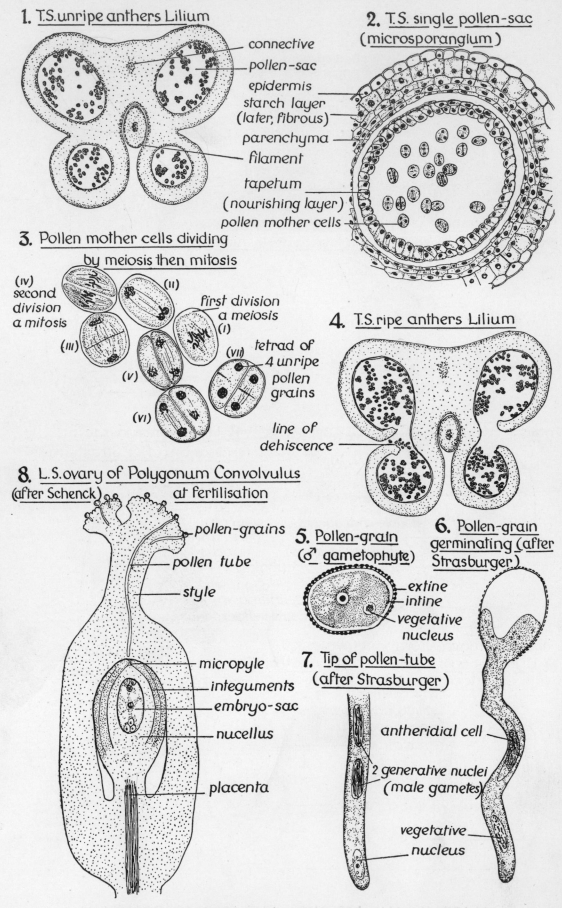

1. T.S. unripe anthers Lilium

connective
pollen-sac
epidermis
starch layer
(later, fibrous)
parenchyma
filament
tapetum
(nourishing layer)
pollen mother cells

2. T.S. single pollen-sac
(microsporangium)

3. Pollen mother cells dividing
by meiosis then mitosis

(IV)
second
division
a mitosis

(II)

(III)

(I)
first division
a meiosis

(V)

(VI)

(VII)
tetrad of
4 unripe
pollen
grains

4. T.S. ripe anthers Lilium

line of
dehiscence

8. L.S. ovary of Polygonum Convolvulus
(after Schenck)   at fertilisation

pollen-grains
pollen tube
style

micropyle
integuments
embryo-sac
nucellus

placenta

5. Pollen-grain
(♂ gametophyte)

extine
intine
vegetative
nucleus

6. Pollen-grain
germinating (after
Strasburger)

7. Tip of pollen-tube
(after Strasburger)

antheridial cell

2 generative nuclei
(male gametes)

vegetative
nucleus

PLATE 62—ANGIOSPERMS : THE MICROSPORANGIUM

Development of Dicotyledonous embryo (Capsella)

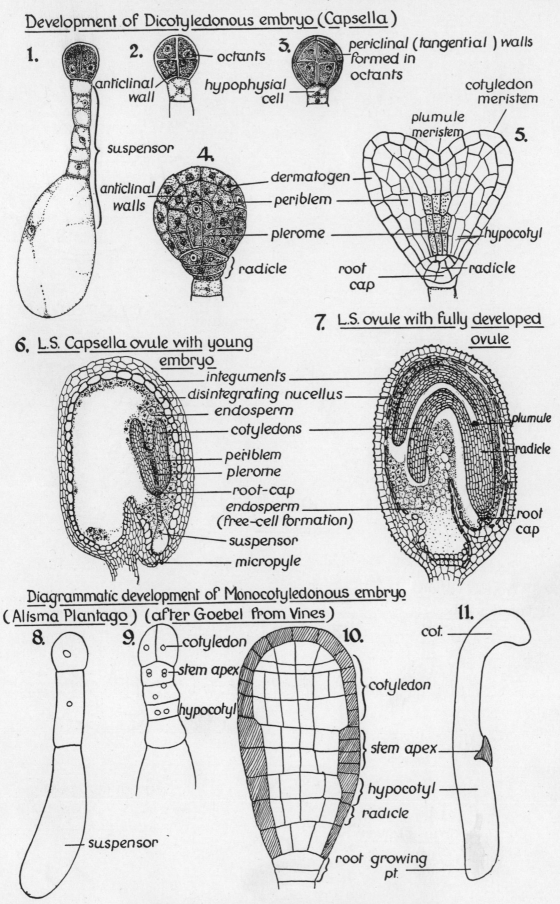

1.
anticlinal wall
suspensor
anticlinal walls

2.
octants
hypophysial cell

3.
periclinal (tangential) walls formed in octants

4.
dermatogen
periblem
plerome
radicle

5.
plumule meristem
cotyledon meristem
hypocotyl
radicle
root cap

6. L.S. Capsella ovule with young embryo
integuments
disintegrating nucellus
endosperm
cotyledons
periblem
plerome
root-cap
endosperm (free-cell formation)
suspensor
micropyle

7. L.S. ovule with fully developed ovule
plumule
radicle
root cap

Diagrammatic development of Monocotyledonous embryo (Alisma Plantago) (after Goebel from Vines)

8.

9.
cotyledon
stem apex
hypocotyl

suspensor

10.
cotyledon
stem apex
hypocotyl
radicle
root growing pt.

11.
cot.

PLATE 63—ANGIOSPERMS : EMBRYOGENY

B.D.—11

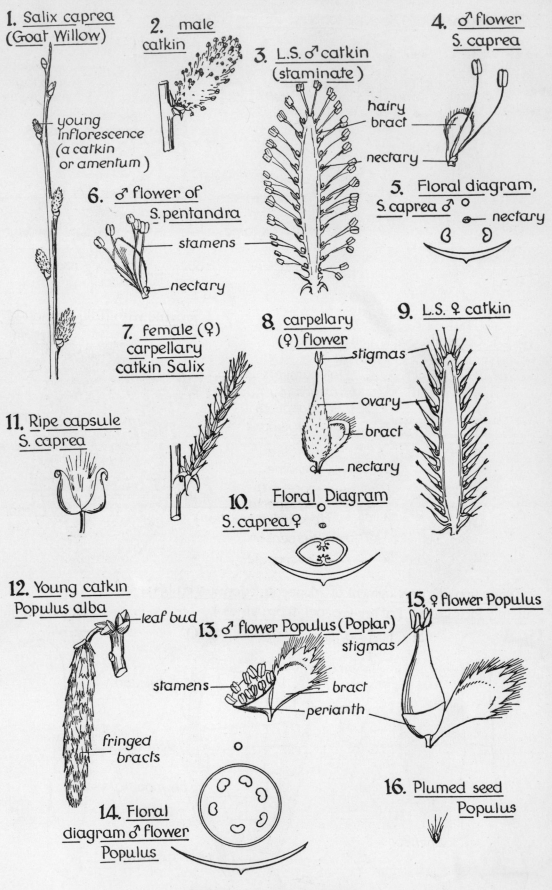

1. Salix caprea (Goat Willow)

young inflorescence (a catkin or amentum)

2. male catkin

3. L.S. ♂ catkin (staminate)

hairy bract

nectary

4. ♂ flower S. caprea

5. Floral diagram, S. caprea ♂ ○

nectary

6. ♂ flower of S. pentandra

stamens

nectary

7. female (♀) carpellary catkin Salix

8. carpellary (♀) flower

stigmas

ovary

bract

nectary

9. L.S. ♀ catkin

11. Ripe capsule S. caprea

10. Floral Diagram S. caprea ♀

12. Young catkin Populus alba

leaf bud

fringed bracts

13. ♂ flower Populus (Poplar)

stigmas

stamens

bract

perianth

14. Floral diagram ♂ flower Populus

15. ♀ flower Populus

16. Plumed seed Populus

PLATE 64—SALICACEÆ

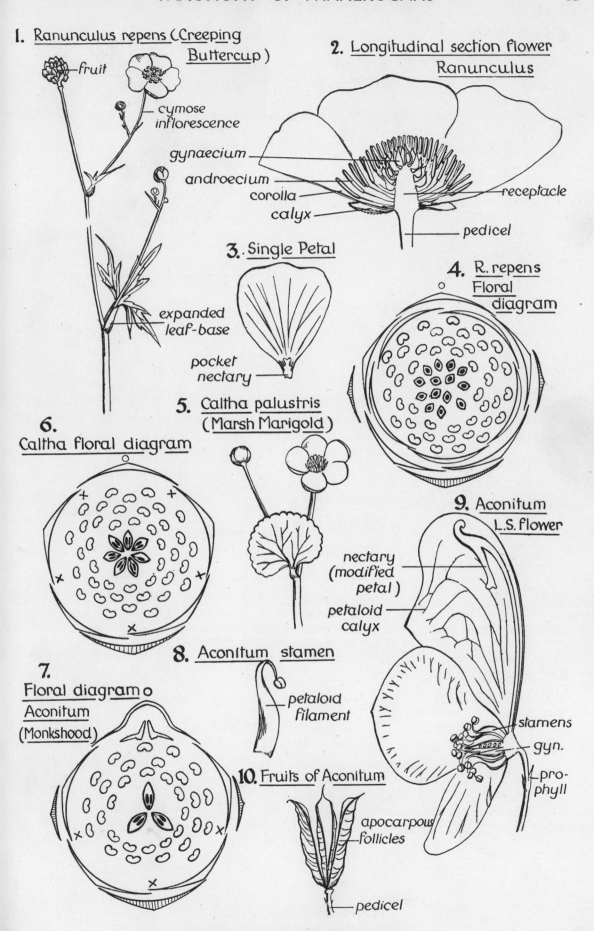

1. Ranunculus repens (Creeping Buttercup)
 —fruit
 cymose inflorescence
 expanded leaf-base

2. Longitudinal section flower Ranunculus
 gynaecium
 androecium
 corolla
 calyx
 receptacle
 pedicel

3. Single Petal
 expanded leaf-base
 pocket nectary

4. R. repens Floral diagram

5. Caltha palustris (Marsh Marigold)

6. Caltha floral diagram

7. Floral diagram Aconitum (Monkshood)

8. Aconitum stamen
 petaloid filament

9. Aconitum L.S. Flower
 nectary (modified petal)
 petaloid calyx
 stamens
 gyn.
 pro-phyll

10. Fruits of Aconitum
 apocarpous follicles
 pedicel

PLATE 65—RANUNCULACEÆ

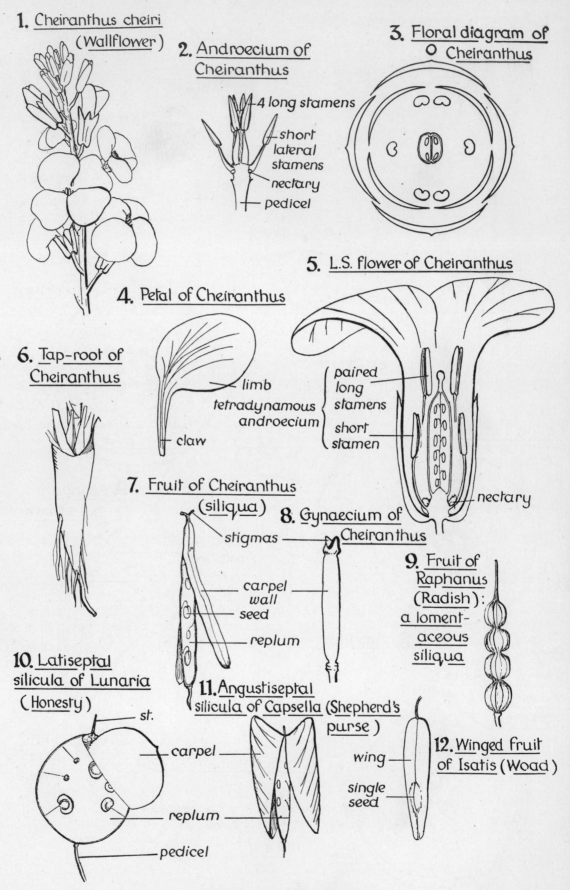

1. Cheiranthus cheiri (Wallflower)

2. Androecium of Cheiranthus
— 4 long stamens
— short lateral stamens
— nectary
— pedicel

3. Floral diagram of Cheiranthus

4. Petal of Cheiranthus
— limb
tetradynamous androecium
— claw

5. L.S. flower of Cheiranthus
paired long stamens
short stamen
— nectary

6. Tap-root of Cheiranthus

7. Fruit of Cheiranthus (siliqua)
stigmas —
carpel wall
seed
replum

8. Gynaecium of Cheiranthus

9. Fruit of Raphanus (Radish): a loment-aceous siliqua

10. Latiseptal silicula of Lunaria (Honesty)
st.
carpel
replum
pedicel

11. Angustiseptal silicula of Capsella (Shepherd's purse)

12. Winged fruit of Isatis (Woad)
wing
single seed

PLATE 66—CRUCIFERÆ

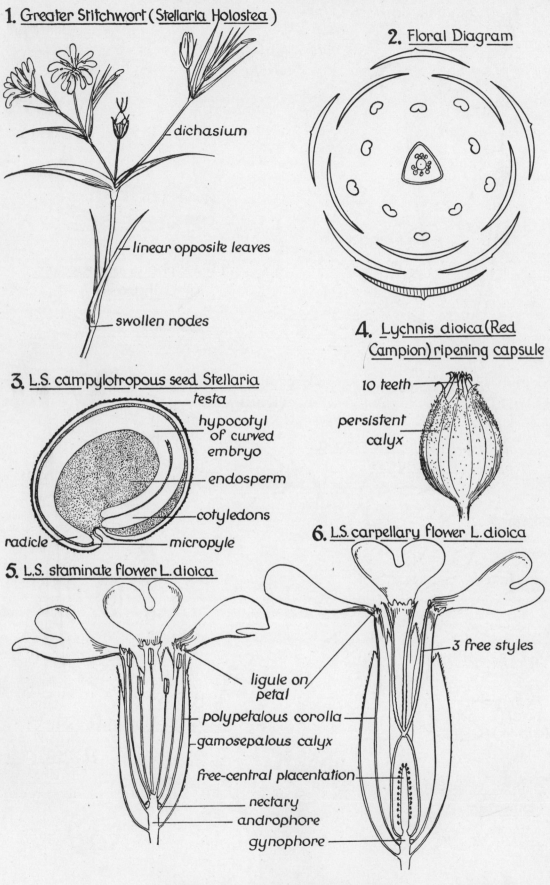

1. Greater Stitchwort (Stellaria Holostea)

dichasium

linear opposite leaves

swollen nodes

2. Floral Diagram

3. L.S. campylotropous seed Stellaria

testa

hypocotyl of curved embryo

endosperm

cotyledons

radicle

micropyle

4. Lychnis dioica (Red Campion) ripening capsule

10 teeth

persistent calyx

6. L.S. carpellary flower L.dioica

3 free styles

5. L.S. staminate flower L.dioica

ligule on petal

polypetalous corolla

gamosepalous calyx

free-central placentation

nectary

androphore

gynophore

PLATE 67—CARYOPHYLLACEÆ

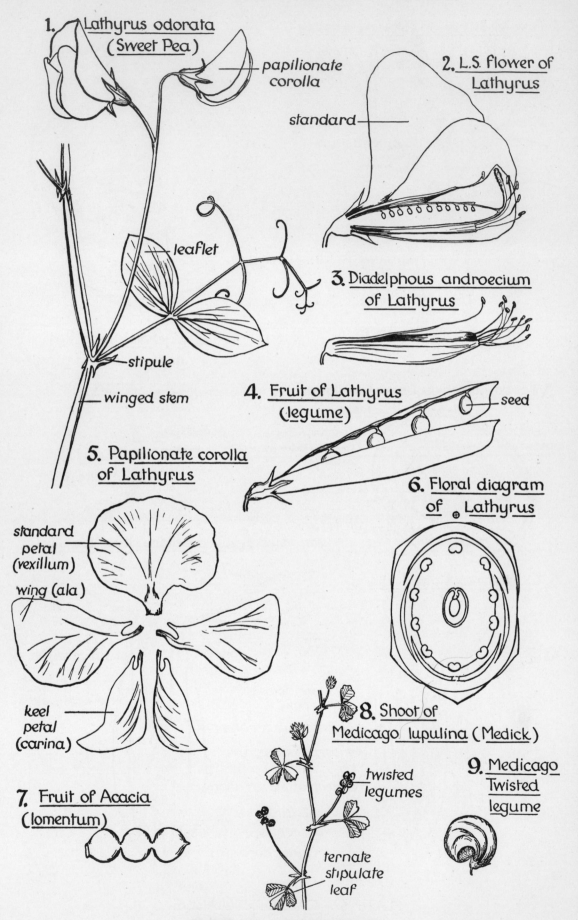

1. Lathyrus odorata (Sweet Pea)

papilionate corolla

2. L.S. flower of Lathyrus

standard

leaflet

stipule

winged stem

3. Diadelphous androecium of Lathyrus

4. Fruit of Lathyrus (legume)

seed

5. Papilionate corolla of Lathyrus

6. Floral diagram of ⊕ Lathyrus

standard petal (vexillum)

wing (ala)

keel petal (carina)

8. Shoot of Medicago lupulina (Medick)

twisted legumes

9. Medicago Twisted legume

7. Fruit of Acacia (lomentum)

ternate stipulate leaf

PLATE 68—LEGUMINOSÆ

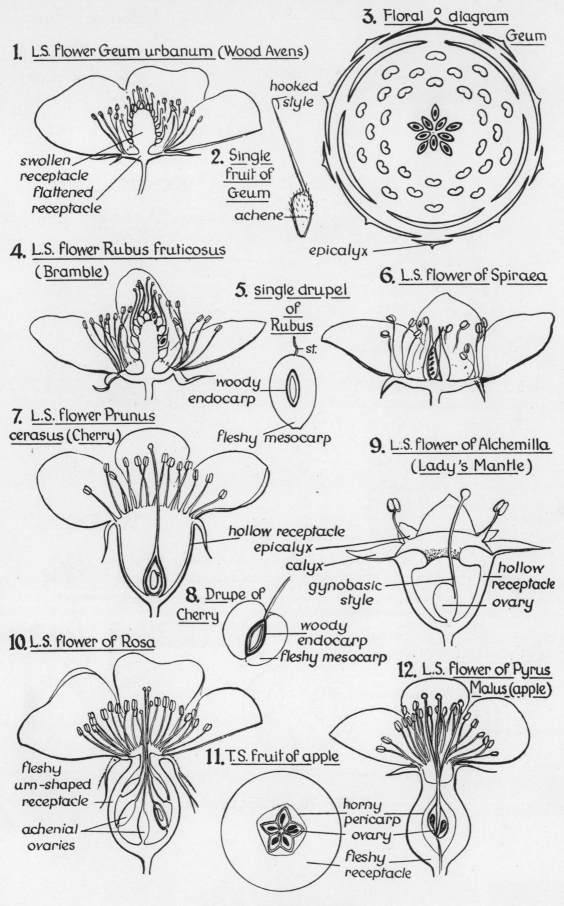

1. L.S. flower Geum urbanum (Wood Avens)

swollen receptacle
flattened receptacle

hooked style

2. Single fruit of Geum
achene

3. Floral diagram
Geum

epicalyx

4. L.S. flower Rubus fruticosus (Bramble)

5. single drupel of Rubus
st.
woody endocarp
fleshy mesocarp

6. L.S. flower of Spiraea

7. L.S. flower Prunus cerasus (Cherry)

hollow receptacle
epicalyx
calyx
gynobasic style

8. Drupe of Cherry
woody endocarp
fleshy mesocarp

9. L.S. flower of Alchemilla (Lady's Mantle)

hollow receptacle
ovary

10. L.S. flower of Rosa

fleshy urn-shaped receptacle

achenial ovaries

11. T.S. fruit of apple

horny pericarp
ovary
fleshy receptacle

12. L.S. flower of Pyrus Malus (apple)

PLATE 69—ROSACEÆ

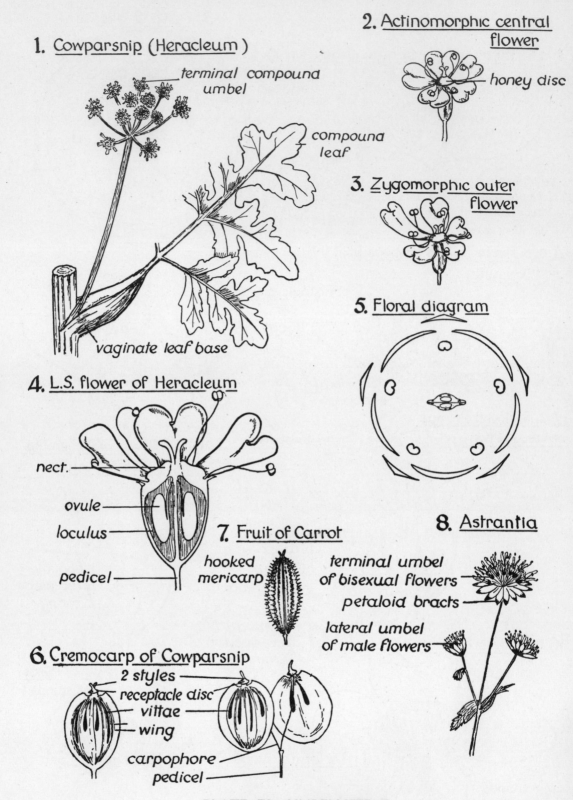

1. Cowparsnip (Heracleum)

terminal compound umbel

compound leaf

vaginate leaf base

2. Actinomorphic central flower

honey disc

3. Zygomorphic outer flower

5. Floral diagram

4. L.S. flower of Heracleum

nect.

ovule

loculus

pedicel

7. Fruit of Carrot

hooked mericarp

8. Astrantia

terminal umbel of bisexual flowers

petaloid bracts

lateral umbel of male flowers

6. Cremocarp of Cowparsnip

2 styles

receptacle disc

vittae

wing

carpophore

pedicel

PLATE 70—UMBELLIFERÆ

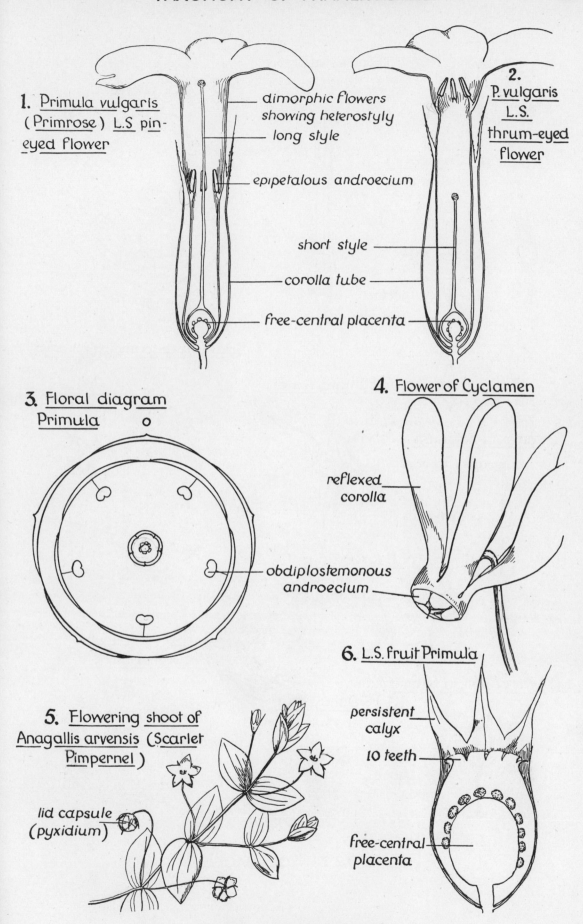

1. Primula vulgaris (Primrose) L.S pin-eyed flower

dimorphic flowers showing heterostyly

long style

epipetalous androecium

2. P. vulgaris L.S. thrum-eyed flower

short style

corolla tube

free-central placenta

3. Floral diagram Primula

obdiplostemonous androecium

4. Flower of Cyclamen

reflexed corolla

obdiplostemonous androecium

5. Flowering shoot of Anagallis arvensis (Scarlet Pimpernel)

lid capsule (pyxidium)

6. L.S. fruit Primula

persistent calyx

10 teeth

free-central placenta

PLATE 71—PRIMULACEÆ

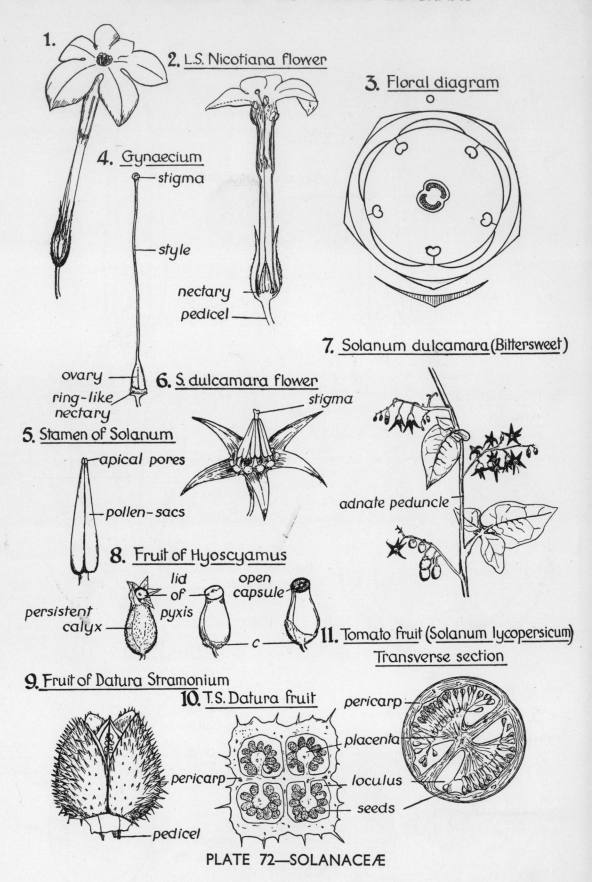

1.

2. L.S. Nicotiana flower

3. Floral diagram

4. Gynaecium
— stigma
— style
nectary
pedicel

ovary
ring-like
nectary

6. S. dulcamara flower
stigma

7. Solanum dulcamara (Bittersweet)

adnate peduncle

5. Stamen of Solanum
apical pores
pollen-sacs

8. Fruit of Hyoscyamus
lid
of
pyxis
open
capsule
persistent
calyx
c

11. Tomato fruit (Solanum lycopersicum)
Transverse section

9. Fruit of Datura Stramonium
10. T.S. Datura fruit

pericarp
placenta
loculus
seeds

pericarp

pedicel

PLATE 72—SOLANACEÆ

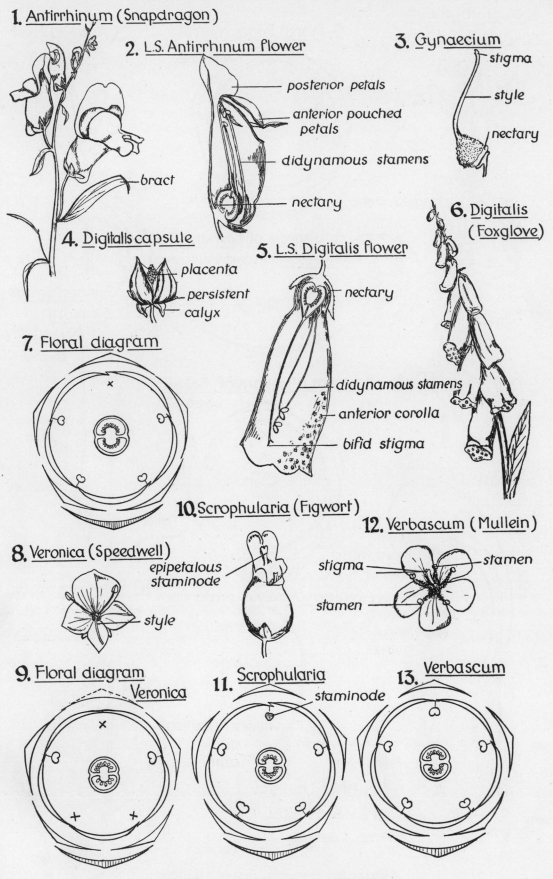

1. Antirrhinum (Snapdragon)

2. L.S. Antirrhinum flower

- posterior petals
- anterior pouched petals
- didynamous stamens
- nectary
- bract

3. Gynaecium

- stigma
- style
- nectary

4. Digitalis capsule

- placenta
- persistent calyx

5. L.S. Digitalis flower

- nectary
- didynamous stamens
- anterior corolla
- bifid stigma

6. Digitalis (Foxglove)

7. Floral diagram

8. Veronica (Speedwell)

- style

10. Scrophularia (Figwort)

- epipetalous staminode

12. Verbascum (Mullein)

- stigma
- stamen
- stamen

9. Floral diagram Veronica

11. Scrophularia

- staminode

13. Verbascum

PLATE 73—SCROPHULARIACEÆ

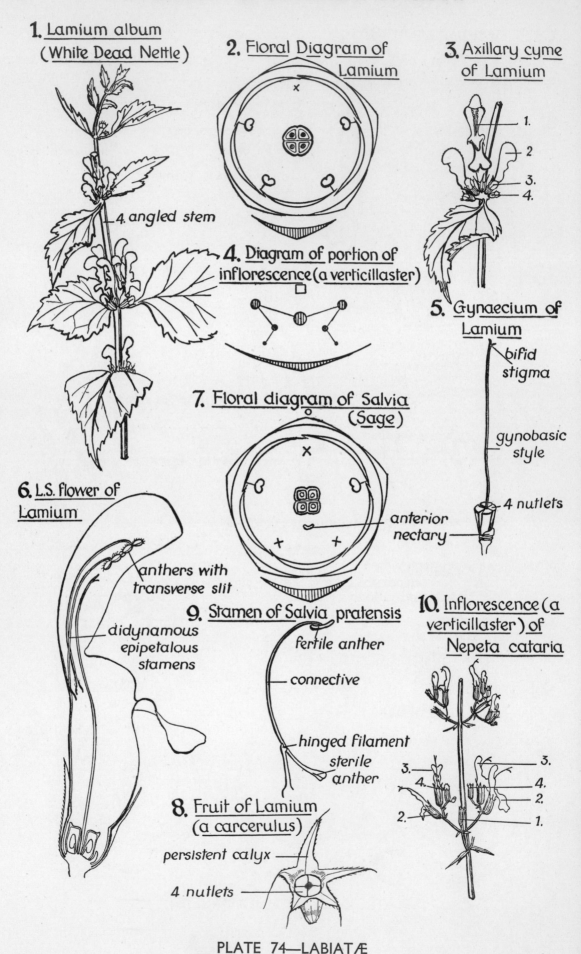

1. Lamium album (White Dead Nettle)

4. angled stem

2. Floral Diagram of Lamium

3. Axillary cyme of Lamium

1.
2
3.
4.

4. Diagram of portion of inflorescence (a verticillaster)

5. Gynaecium of Lamium

bifid stigma

gynobasic style

4 nutlets

7. Floral diagram of Salvia (Sage)

anterior nectary

6. L.S. flower of Lamium

anthers with transverse slit

didynamous epipetalous stamens

9. Stamen of Salvia pratensis

fertile anther

connective

hinged filament sterile anther

10. Inflorescence (a verticillaster) of Nepeta cataria

3.
4.

3.
4.
2.
1.

2.

8. Fruit of Lamium (a carcerulus)

persistent calyx

4 nutlets

PLATE 74—LABIATÆ

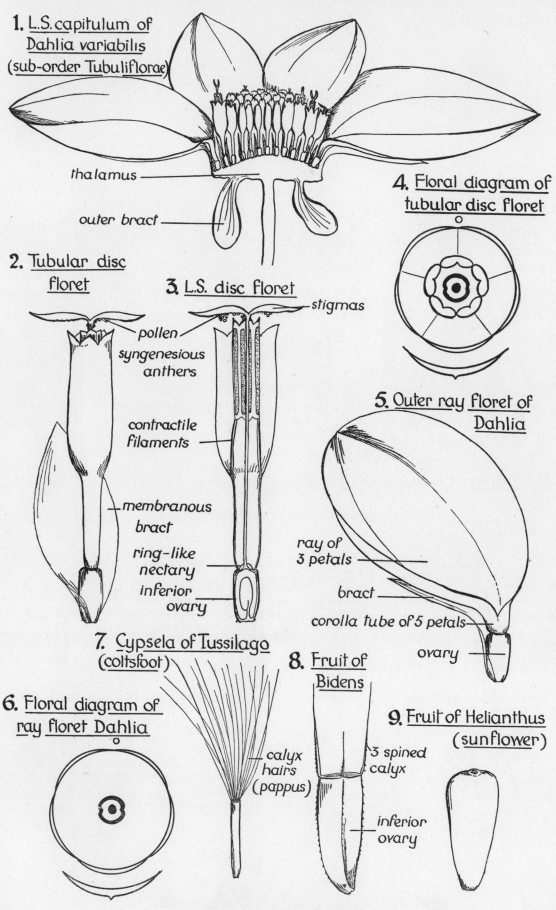

1. L.S. capitulum of Dahlia variabilis (sub-order Tubuliflorae)

thalamus

outer bract

2. Tubular disc floret

3. L.S. disc floret

stigmas

pollen

syngenesious anthers

contractile filaments

membranous bract

ring-like nectary

inferior ovary

4. Floral diagram of tubular disc floret

5. Outer ray floret of Dahlia

ray of 3 petals

bract

corolla tube of 5 petals

ovary

7. Cypsela of Tussilago (coltsfoot)

calyx hairs (pappus)

8. Fruit of Bidens

3 spined calyx

inferior ovary

9. Fruit of Helianthus (sunflower)

6. Floral diagram of ray floret Dahlia

PLATE 75—COMPOSITÆ

1. Centaurea cyanea (Cornflower)

2. Sterile (neuter) floret

3. Bisexual floret

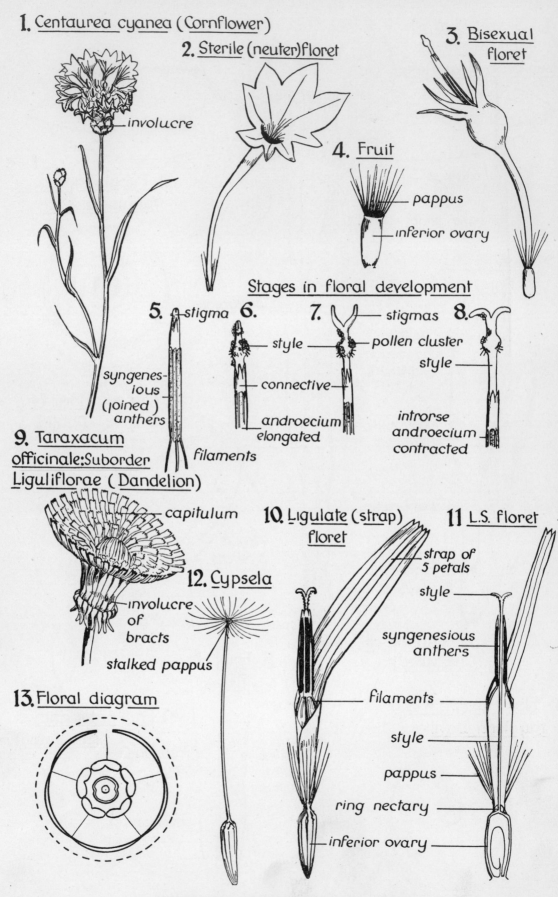

involucre

4. Fruit

pappus

inferior ovary

Stages in floral development

5. stigma

6.

7. stigmas

8.

syngenes-
ious
(joined)
anthers

style

pollen cluster

style

connective

filaments

androecium
elongated

introrse
androecium
contracted

9. Taraxacum
officinale: Suborder
Liguliflorae (Dandelion)

capitulum

10. Ligulate (strap)
floret

11. L.S. floret

strap of
5 petals

style

12. Cypsela

involucre
of
bracts

syngenesious
anthers

filaments

stalked pappus

style

13. Floral diagram

pappus

ring nectary

inferior ovary

PLATE 76—COMPOSITÆ—Continued

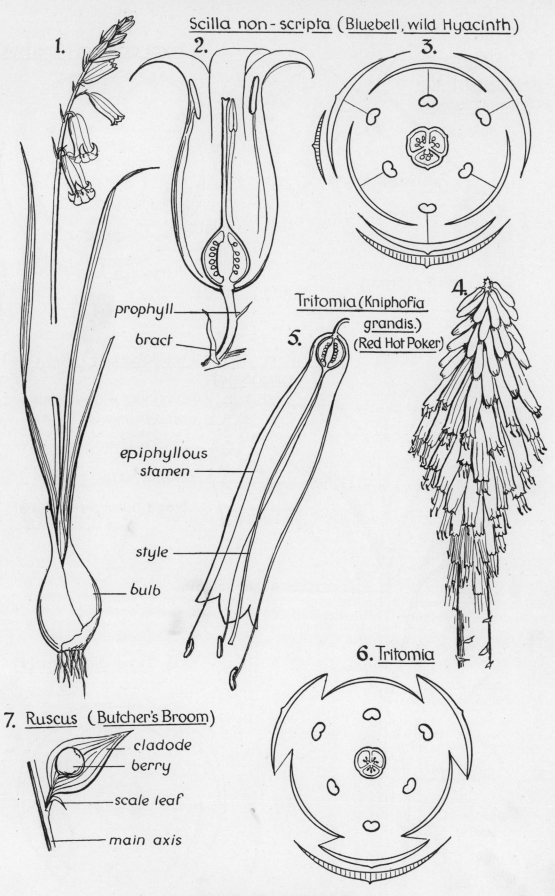

Scilla non-scripta (Bluebell, wild Hyacinth)

1.

2.

3.

prophyll
bract

Tritomia (Kniphofia grandis.) (Red Hot Poker)

5.

4.

epiphyllous stamen

style

bulb

6. Tritomia

7. Ruscus (Butcher's Broom)
cladode
berry
scale leaf
main axis

PLATE 77—LILIACEÆ

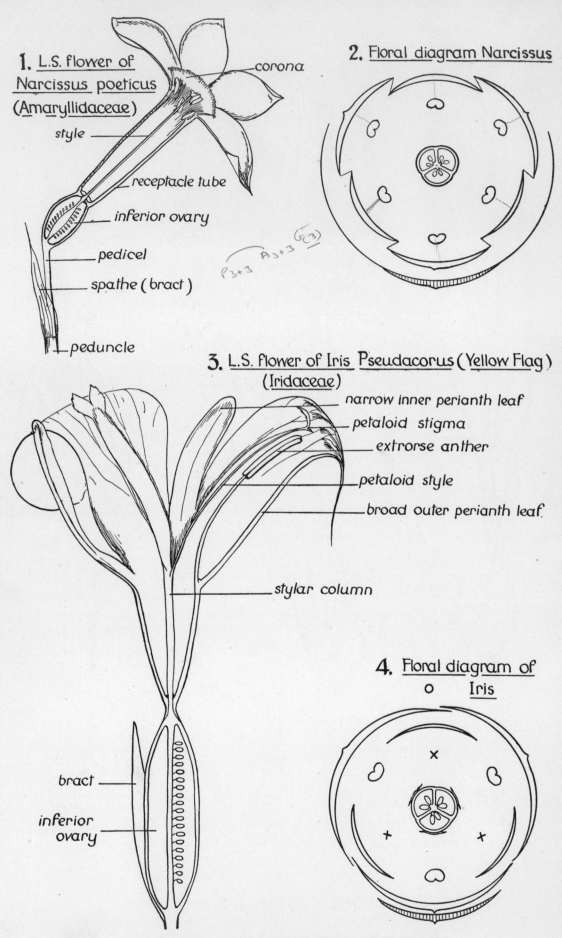

1. L.S. flower of Narcissus poeticus (Amaryllidaceae)

— corona
— style
— receptacle tube
— inferior ovary
— pedicel
— spathe (bract)
— peduncle

P3+3 A3+3 G(3)

2. Floral diagram Narcissus

3. L.S. flower of Iris Pseudacorus (Yellow Flag) (Iridaceae)

— narrow inner perianth leaf
— petaloid stigma
— extrorse anther
— petaloid style
— broad outer perianth leaf

— stylar column

bract
inferior ovary

4. Floral diagram of Iris

PLATE 78—AMARYLLIDACEÆ : IRIDACEÆ

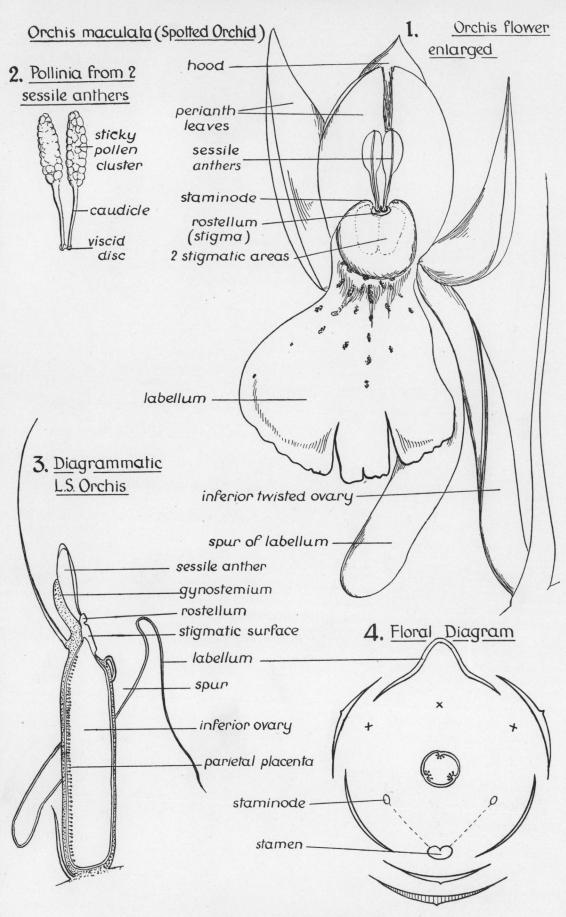

Orchis maculata (Spotted Orchid)

2. Pollinia from 2 sessile anthers

sticky pollen cluster

caudicle

viscid disc

1. Orchis flower enlarged

hood

perianth leaves

sessile anthers

staminode

rostellum (stigma)

2 stigmatic areas

labellum

inferior twisted ovary

spur of labellum

3. Diagrammatic L.S. Orchis

sessile anther

gynostemium

rostellum

stigmatic surface

labellum

spur

inferior ovary

parietal placenta

4. Floral Diagram

staminode

stamen

PLATE 79—ORCHIDACEÆ

B.D.—13

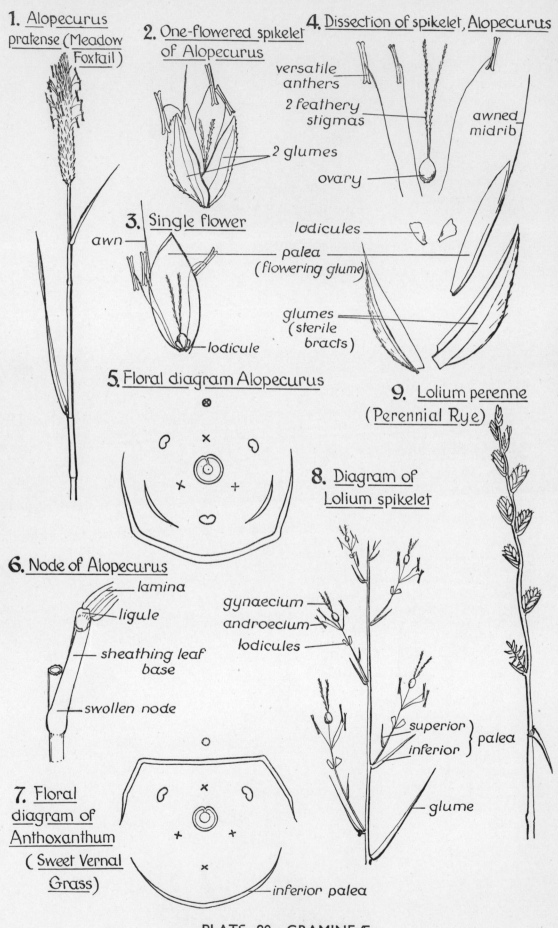

1. Alopecurus pratense (Meadow Foxtail)

2. One-flowered spikelet of Alopecurus

2 glumes

4. Dissection of spikelet, Alopecurus

versatile anthers

2 feathery stigmas

ovary

awned midrib

3. Single flower

awn

lodicules

palea (flowering glume)

glumes (sterile bracts)

lodicule

5. Floral diagram Alopecurus

9. Lolium perenne (Perennial Rye)

8. Diagram of Lolium spikelet

gynaecium

androecium

lodicules

superior
inferior } palea

glume

6. Node of Alopecurus

lamina

ligule

sheathing leaf base

swollen node

7. Floral diagram of Anthoxanthum (Sweet Vernal Grass)

inferior palea

PLATE 80—GRAMINEÆ

INDEX

Abaxial, 55, 56
Absciss layer, 12
Acacia, 18, 86
Acer, 17, 24
Achene, 23, 24, 87
Acicular, 16
Aconitum, 24, 83
Acorn (see Quercus), 23
Actinomorphic, 21, 88
Acuminate, 16, 54
Acute apex, 16
Adaxial, 55, 56
Adnate, 16, 23, 90
Adventitious, 11, 12, 13, 14, 78
Aerial root, 11, 49
Æsculus, 12
Æstivation, 20
Agaricus, 64
Aggregate fruit (see Drupels), 23
Air bladder, 62
  ,, sac, 77
  ,, space, 35, 47, 50, 53, 54, 55, 64, 70, 71
Ala, 86
Albuminoid cells, 57, 78
Albuminous (see Endospermous), 26, 72
Alchemilla, 22, 87
Aleurone grains, 31, 72
Alisma, 81
Allium, 12, 27, 33
Alopecurus, 98
Alternate leaves, 17
Amaryllidaceæ, 96
Amentum, 19, 82
Ampelopsis (see Virginian Creeper), 15
Amphitrich, 63
Amplexicaul, 16
Anagallis, 89
Anatropous, 79
Andrœcium, 20, 21, 83–98
Androgonidium, 61
Androphore, 85
Anemone, 22
Angiosperms, 79–98
Angustiseptal, 84
Annular rings, 40
Annular vessels, 34, 35, 39
Annulus, 64, 67, 69, 70
Anterior plane, 20, 21
Anthemis, 19
Anther, 21, 80

Antheridium, 61, 62, 65, 66, 69, 70, 75, 77
Antherozoids (see Spermatozoids), 61, 62, 66, 72
Anthoxanthum, 98
Anthrax (see B. anthracis), 63
Anticlinal, 81
Antipodal cells, 79
Antirrhinum, 24, 91
Apical meristem, 33, 69
Apocarpous, 22, 83
Apple, 87
Archegonium, 65, 66, 69, 72, 76
Archesporium, 67
Aril, 26, 78
Artichoke, Jerusalem, 13
Arum, 17, 19
Ascospores, 63
Ascus, 63
Asexual, 61, 63
Ash (see Fraxinus), 23
Asparagus, 14
Asparagus " fern," 14
Asperula, 17
Aspidium, 68, 69
Assimilating layer, 62, 66, 67
Astrantia, 88
Atropa (see Belladonna), 31
Autumn wood, 40, 42, 43
Avena (see Oat), 31
Avens, 87
Awn, 98
Axile, 22
Axillary bud, 12, 13

Bacillus, 63
  ,,   anthracis, 63
  ,,   tetani, 63
  ,,   radicicola, 63
Bacteria, 63
Bacteroid, 63
Bark (see Periderm), 40, 42, 43, 46
Basidium, 64
Basifixed, 21
Bast (see Phloem), 35, 57, 68, 70, 71
  ,, fibres, 43
Bean (see Vicia), 21, 25, 31, 32, 51, 52
Belladonna, 31
Bellis, 16
Berry, 23, 95
Bicollateral bundles, 38, 55

99

NOTES

NOTES

NOTES

NOTES